THE QUIZ BOOK COMPANY

First published in 2004 by
The Quiz Book Company Ltd
Bardfield Centre,
Great Bardfield, Essex, CM7 4SL

2 4 6 8 10 9 7 5 3 1

ISBN 1-84236-502-9

Printed in India

Questions written by Chris Rigby.

QUIZ 1

1. Which county did Hilda Ogden move to when she left Weatherfield?
2. Which star of *Dynasty* died of AIDS in 1985?
3. Angie Watts left Walford for the sunnier climes of which country?
4. In which soap was the entire cast culled in a boating accident to enable the producers to introduce a new cast?
5. Who was the first character to die in *Coronation Street*?
6. Who left Albert Square in 2004, after his sister Janine's murder confession?
7. Which Weatherfield resident died in his sleep on New Year's Day 1999?
8. How did Trevor Morgan die in *EastEnders*?
9. Who was the only actor to appear in the first episode of *Brookside* and the final farewell episode in 2003?
10. Which member of the Colby family was abducted by aliens?

ANSWERS

1. Derbyshire 2. Rock Hudson 3. Spain 4. *Family Affairs* 5. May Hardman 6. Ricky Butcher 7. Alf Roberts 8. In a fire 9. Paul Usher (who played Barry Grant) 10. Fallon Colby

QUIZ 2

1. Which former *Dad's Army* star plays the character of Derek Harkinson in *EastEnders*?
2. Who plays the role of Emily Bishop in *Coronation Street*?
3. In which soap did the cricket star Freddie Trueman appear as himself?
4. How was Jock Ewing killed in *Dallas*?
5. Which TV series was set in a boatyard called The Mermaid?
6. In *EastEnders*, what is the name of the son of Pete and Kathy Beale?
7. In which US soap did Henry Kissinger and Gerald Ford appear as themselves?
8. Who played a porter called Jimmy Powell in *Casualty*?
9. *Midland Road* was the original working title of which soap?
10. The Lamonts and the Taylors are two families that feature in which Scottish-based soap?

ANSWERS

1. Ian Lavender 2. Eileen Derbyshire 3. *Emmerdale Farm* 4. In a helicopter crash 5. *Howard's Way* 6. Ian 7. *Dynasty* 8. Robson Green 9. *Crossroads* 10. *Take The High Road*

QUIZ 3

1 What is the first name of the *EastEnders* character whose surnames have been Harris, Beale, Wicks and Butcher?

2 What was the original intended title of *Coronation Street*?

3 Who played Doris Luke in *Crossroads*, but became better known on TV for her wrinkled stockings?

4 *In Coronation Street*, which wife of Ken Barlow committed suicide by drug overdose?

5 Which Liverpool hotel was the subject of a 1998 BBC docu-soap?

6 What was the name of the hospital in the medical soap *Angels*?

7 Which series is set in the Yorkshire town of Skelthwaite?

8 Which *EastEnders* character is nicknamed Little Mo?

9 Which much-maligned soap was set in the Spanish resort of Los Barcos?

10 In 1990 which character from *EastEnders* won a £10,000 bingo jackpot?

ANSWERS

1. Pat 2. *Florizel Street* 3. Kathy Staff 4. Janet 5. The Adelphi 6. St Angela's 7. *Where The Heart Is* 8. Maureen Mitchell 9. *Eldorado* 10. Dot Cotton

QUIZ 4

1. Why were soap operas so named?
2. Which soap, set in New England, was the first US soap to be sold to the UK?
3. Which 1960s soap featured the farm-dwelling Cooper family?
4. Who played the title role in the medical drama *Dr Kildare*?
5. Who played the role of Lou Beale in the early days of *EastEnders*?
6. Which series was set at Oxbridge General Hospital?
7. In *Coronation Street*, who married Nellie Briggs and Rita Littlewood?
8. In which TV show of the 1960s did Kathleen Harrison play a cleaning lady who inherited her boss's fortune?
9. In which soap, set in the 1800s, did Barbara Stanwyck play the role of Victoria Barkley?
10. Who played Minnie Caldwell for 16 years in *Coronation Street*?

ANSWERS

1. They were originally sponsored by soap manufacturers 2. *Peyton Place* 3. *The Newcomers* 4. Richard Chamberlain 5. Anna Wing 6. *Emergency Ward 10* 7. Len Fairclough 8. *Mrs Thursday* 9. *The Big Valley* 10. Margot Bryant

QUIZ 5

1 Which TV soap theme provided Mark Williams and Karen Boddington with a chart hit in 1989?

2 What was the name of the central family in *When The Boat Comes In*?

3 Which actress, famed for playing a soap pub landlady, won the Rear Of The Year Award in 1987?

4 In which spoof soap did Julie Walters play the role of Mrs Overall?

5 On whose novels was the TV show *The Darling Buds Of May* based?

6 Which former star of *EastEnders* went on to play a barrister in the legal drama *In Defence*?

7 In *Coronation Street*, which foreign country did Elsie Howard and Bill Gregory leave the street for?

8 What is the first name of Spider Nugent in *Coronation Street*?

9 What is the name of the co-creator of *EastEnders* who died in 1997 aged 69?

10 What was the name of the wine bar owned by James Wilmot-Brown that was burned down in *EastEnders*?

ANSWERS

1. *Home And Away* 2. Seaton 3. Anita Dobson 4. *Acorn Antiques* 5. H E Bates 6. Ross Kemp 7. Portugal 8. Geoffrey 9. Julia Smith 10. The Dagmar

QUIZ 6

1. Which TV sitcom co-starred former *Coronation Street* star Sarah Lancashire and former *Casualty* star Clive Mantle?
2. Which Oscar-winning actress played the role of Helena Cassadine in the US soap *General Hospital*?
3. Who created *Brookside*?
4. In which 1970s Australian soap did Kylie Minogue and Jason Donovan play brother and sister?
5. Which soap features a newspaper called the *Hotten Courier*?
6. In *Coronation Street* who was Deidre Hunt's first husband?
7. Which actor left *EastEnders* and went on to star in the sci-fi drama *Crime Traveller*?
8. Who played the role of Brenda Walsh in *Beverly Hills 90210*?
9. Which soap had the original working title of *Oil*?
10. Who played The Chinese Detective on TV before landing the role of Michael Choi in *Brookside*?

ANSWERS

1. *Bloomin' Marvellous* 2. Elizabeth Taylor 3. Phil Redmond 4. *Skyways* 5. *Emmerdale* 6. Ray Langton 7. Michael French 8. Shannen Doherty 9. *Dynasty* 10. David Yip

QUIZ 7

Identify the soap operas from the surnames of three of the central families.

1 Grant, Collins and Harrison

2 Karim, Osman and Jackson

3 Lockhead, Svendson and Fernandez

4 Blaisdel, Carrington and Dexter

5 Fletcher, Simpson and Roberts

6 Gioberti, Cumson and Channing

7 Platt, Clegg and Mallett

8 Mangel, Bishop and Clarke

9 Jarvis, Harvey and Pollard

10 Avery, Ward and Fairgate

ANSWERS

1. *Brookside* 2. *EastEnders* 3. *Eldorado* 4. *Dynasty* 5. *Home And Away* 6. *Falcon Crest* 7. *Coronation Street* 8. *Neighbours* 9. *Crossroads* 10. *Knot's Landing*

QUIZ 8

1. Which former *Coronation Street* actress went on to play the role of Jean in the sitcom *Dinnerladies*?
2. Which character died in the very first episode of *EastEnders*?
3. Which soap features a nightclub called The Loft?
4. In which year was *Home And Away* first screened on British TV?
5. Who played the role of Sue Ellen in *Dallas*?
6. How many children did John and Olivia have in *The Waltons*?
7. What is the name of the fictional football team in the football soap *Dream Team*?
8. Who played the title role in *The District Nurse*?
9. Which role in *Coronation Street* is played by David Neilson?
10. What is the title of the TV soap that co-stars Gareth Hunt, Lesley Joseph and Joe McGann?

ANSWERS

1. Anne Reid 2. Reg Cox 3. *Hollyoaks* 4. 1989 5. Linda Gray 6. Seven 7. *Harchester United* 8. Nerys Hughes 9. Roy Cropper 10. *Night And Day*

QUIZ 9

1. In which decade was *The Nanny,* starring Wendy Craig, set?
2. Which Queen Vic landlord was murdered in 1991?
3. What was the name of the travel agency run by Alec Gilroy in *Coronation Street*?
4. On whose novel was the TV series *Brideshead Revisited* based?
5. Which former *Coronation Street* star played the brother-in-law of Hyacinth Bucket in *Keeping Up Appearances*?
6. Which character did Peter Davison play in *All Creatures Great And Small*?
7. In *Coronation Street*, of which pub was Stella Rigby the landlady?
8. Which *EastEnders* star penned an autobiography entitled *True* in 2000?
9. In *Coronation Street,* what was the maiden name of Emily Bishop?
10. Which medical drama featured hospital wards called the Crippen Ward and the Mengele Ward?

ANSWERS

1. 1930s 2. Eddie Royle 3. Sunliners 4. Evelyn Waugh 5. Geoffrey Hughes 6. Tristan Farnon 7. The White Swan 8. Martin Kemp 9. Nugent 10. *Cardiac Arrest*

QUIZ 10

1 What was the name of Dirty Den's giant poodle in *EastEnders*?

2 In *Coronation Street* who shared a home with Alice Pickens and a mynah bird called Kitchener?

3 What is the name of Robbie Jackson's alsatian in *EastEnders*?

4 What was the name of Dorothy and Toby's pet labrador in *Neigbours*?

5 In which TV series did the Ingalls family own a pet dog called Jack?

6 What was the name of Tyrone's pet greyhound in *Coronation Street*?

7 In *Heartbeat* what is the name of Greengrass's pet pooch?

8 In *Coronation Street* what was the name of Percy Sugden's pet budgie?

9 In *EastEnders* who owned a pug dog called Willy?

10 What was the name of the Waltons' pet dog?

ANSWERS

1. Roly 2. Albert Tatlock 3. Wellard 4. Bouncer 5. *Little House On The Prairie* 6. Monica 7. Alfred 8. Randy 9. Ethel Skinner 10. Reckless

QUIZ 11

1. In what year did Meg Richardson wave goodbye to *Crossroads*?
2. What was the name of the family that lived upstairs in *Upstairs Downstairs*?
3. Which supermarket was managed by Reg Holdsworth and Curly Watts?
4. In what year did *Emmerdale Farm* change its name to *Emmerdale*?
5. In which Liverpool suburb was *Brookside* set?
6. In which series did Tazmin Outhwaite play the role of Sergeant Jo McDonagh?
7. Which former pop star played Ros Thorne in *EastEnders*?
8. In which series of the 1970s did Frank Finlay play Peter Manson?
9. What London landmark was added to the opening credits of *EastEnders* in 2000?
10. In which soap mini series did Robert Mitchum play Commander Pug Mitchell?

ANSWERS

1. 1981 2. The Bellamys 3. Bettabuys 4. 1989 5. Croxteth 6. *Red Cap*
7. Clare Grogan 8. *A Bouquet Of Barbed Wire* 9. The Millennium Dome
10. *The Winds Of War*

QUIZ 12

1. In which TV pub can the customers sample the delights of Betty's hotpot?
2. Which *Brookside* character died following a stabbing incident in the city of York?
3. Which *EastEnders* market stall trader was diagnosed HIV positive?
4. In *Dr Finlay's Casebook,* what is the first name of Dr Finlay?
5. In *Dallas*, who is the illegitimate son of Jock Ewing?
6. What is the name of the police station in which *The Bill* is set?
7. Who played Miss Georgina Wolsey in *Upstairs Downstairs*?
8. Which character owned a dog called Trickie Woo in *All Creatures Great And Small*?
9. Zak, Mandy and Butch are all members of which soap family?
10. In *Coronation Street*, who played the mother of Tyrone Dobbs?

ANSWERS

1. Rovers Return 2. Damon Grant 3. Mark Fowler 4. Alan 5. Ray Krebbs 6. Sun Hill 7. Lesley Anne Down 8. Mrs Pumphrey 9. The Dingles 10. Margi Clarke

QUIZ 13

1 Who returned to *EastEnders* in 2003 with the words "Hello princess"?

2 Which *Coronation Street* villain was killed in a collision with a Blackpool tram?

3 Which soap featured a sadistic character called Vera Bennett?

4 Who played JR Ewing?

5 Which *Emmerdale* villain was confined to a wheelchair?

6 Who played the role of Marcus Tandy, the villain of the piece in *Eldorado*?

7 Which actor portrayed nasty Nick Cotton in *EastEnders*?

8 Which character was *Coronation Street*'s first serial killer?

9 Which *Coronation Street* villain was played by Lee Boardman?

10 Who played the role of 'Tricky Dicky' Cole in *EastEnders*?

ANSWERS

1. Dirty Den Watts 2. Alan Bradley 3. *Prisoner Cell Block H* 4. Larry Hagman 5. Chris Tate 6. Jesse Birdsall 7. John Altman 8. Richard Hillman 9. Jez Quigley 10. Ian Reddington

QUIZ 14

1. Who played Annie Sugden for many years in *Emmerdale Farm*?
2. What was the name of the son adopted by Pamela and Bobby Ewing?
3. Which TV company makes *Coronation Street*?
4. Which actor played Tosh Lines in *The Bill*?
5. How did Pete Beale die in *EastEnders*?
6. After leaving *EastEnders*, which actor became the co-owner of The Paradise Club?
7. Which series concentrates on the activities of B25 Blue Watch?
8. The soap mini series *North And South* was set during which conflict?
9. Who created *ER* and went on to write the novel *Jurassic Park*?
10. Which character came to the rescue of Bet Lynch when the Rovers Return went up in flames?

ANSWERS

1. Sheila Mercer 2. Christopher 3. Granada 4. Kevin Lloyd 5. In a car crash 6. Leslie Grantham 7. *London's Burning* 8. The American Civil War 9. Michael Crichton 10. Kevin Webster

QUIZ 15

1 Which member of the Nolan Sisters joined the cast of *Brookside*?

2 What was the name of Fallon's nightclub in *Dynasty*?

3 On whose novel was the 1960s soap *Peyton Place* based?

4 Who is the real life mother of soap actor Larry Hagman?

5 What is the name of the country estate in *Monarch Of The Glen*?

6 Which soap character opened a catering business called The Meal Machine?

7 Who played Mrs Muddle in the children's series *Pipkins* before joining the cast of *Coronation Street*?

8 In which century was *The Onedin Line* set?

9 In *EastEnders*, who was crowned Miss Queen Vic in 1992?

10 What was the name of the hotel run by the Duchess of Duke Street?

ANSWERS

1. Bernadette Nolan 2. Le Mirage 3. Grace Metalious 4. Mary Martin 5. Glenbogle 6. Ian Beale 7. Sue Nicholls 8. 19th century 9. Sam Butcher 10. The Bentinck Hotel

QUIZ 16

1. Who played Dr Chandler in *St Elsewhere* and went on to become an Oscar-winning movie star?
2. Who played John Boy's father in *The Waltons*?
3. In which US state is *Dawson's Creek* set?
4. Which show won eight Emmy Awards in 1995?
5. Who played Krystle Carrington in *Dynasty*?
6. In which city is *Baywatch* set?
7. Which character was played by Ken Kercheval in *Dallas*?
8. In the soap mini-series *Rich Man, Poor Man*, Peter Strauss played the rich man. Who played the poor man?
9. In which series did Harry Hamlin play Michael Kuzak?
10. Which series was set in the Alaskan town of Cicely?

ANSWERS

1. Denzel Washington 2. Ralph Waite 3. Massachusetts 4. *ER* 5. Linda Evans 6. Los Angeles 7. Cliff Barnes 8. Nick Nolte 9. *LA Law* 10. *Northern Exposure*

QUIZ 17

1. In *Emmerdale*, who killed Harry Mowlem?
2. Who plays the ever-reliable Charlie Fairhead in *Casualty*?
3. In which decade was *The House Of Elliott* set?
4. In which country was the Channel 4 soap *Black Forest Clinic* set?
5. Which ITV soap was launched in 1985 and only lasted for 100 episodes?
6. Who married Gail Tilsley in 1991?
7. Who played the role of Ernie Bishop in *Coronation Street*?
8. What did the TV show *The Class Of Beverly Hills* change its title to?
9. Who did Deidre Barlow have a much-hyped affair with in 1983?
10. Who provided the voice of Charlie in *Charlie's Angels* and went on to land a leading role in *Dynasty*?

ANSWERS

1. Derek Walker 2. Derek Thompson 3. 1920s 4. Germany 5. *Albion Market* 6. Martin Platt 7. Stephen Hancock 8. *Beverly Hills 90210* 9. Mike Baldwin 10. John Forsythe

QUIZ 18

1. Who played the mother of Steve Owen in *EastEnders*?
2. In which series did Liza Goddard play the role of April Merroney?
3. Who, early in her showbiz career, played the role of Caroline Winthrop in *Crossroads*?
4. In which series did *EastEnders* star Letitia Dean play a telephonist?
5. The very first episode of which soap opened with the funeral of Jacob Sugden?
6. On whose novel was *The Jewel In The Crown* based?
7. Which ex-Page Three girl joined the cast of *Brookside* in the role of Frankie?
8. What is the first name of Dr Quinn Medicine Woman?
9. In *Coronation Street* what was the maiden name of Sally Webster?
10. Who played Inspector Barlow in *Z Cars*?

ANSWERS

1. Sheila Hancock 2. *The Brothers* 3. Elaine Paige 4. *The Hello Girls* 5. *Emmerdale Farm* 6. Paul Scott 7. Linda Lusardi 8. Michaela 9. Seddon 10. Stratford Johns

QUIZ 19

1. Which character was played by John Forsythe in *Dynasty*?
2. Which *Dallas* character was nicknamed The Poisoned Dwarf by Terry Wogan?
3. Who played Alison McKenzie in *Peyton Place* before becoming a major Hollywood star?
4. Which is the home state of *The Waltons*?
5. In which US state is *Sweet Valley High* set?
6. Which US soap featured an underworld gang called The Thirteen?
7. Which former member of *The Partridge Family* played Grace Van Owen in *LA Law*?
8. Who played the role of Caroline Holden in *Baywatch*?
9. Carrie, Samantha, Miranda and Charlotte were the four main characters in which TV series?
10. 'Three Stars Will Shine Tonight' is the title of the theme song of which TV series?

ANSWERS

1. Blake Carrington 2. Lucy Ewing 3. Mia Farrow 4. Virginia 5. California 6. *Falcon Crest* 7. Susan Dey 8. Yasmin Bleeth 9. *Sex And The City* 10. *Dr Kildare*

QUIZ 20

1. Which member of the glam rock group Slade played the cameo role of Stan Potter in *Coronation Street*?
2. In which English county was *A Bouquet Of Barbed Wire* set?
3. Which confectionary company sponsors *Coronation Street*?
4. Who played Karen Buckley in *Where The Heart Is*?
5. In which fictional town is the *Crossroads Motel* located?
6. Which former *Coronation Street* star became the stepmother of Cherie Blair?
7. In the UK 1970s soap *General Hospital* what was the name of the hospital?
8. In 1993 the cast of which soap was decimated by a plane crash?
9. Who plays the role of Ricky Butcher in *EastEnders*?
10. What is the first name of Dr Kildare?

ANSWERS

1. Noddy Holder 2. Surrey 3. Cadbury's 4. Leslie Ash 5. King's Oak 6. Pat Phoenix 7. Midland General 8. *Emmerdale* 9. Sid Owen 10. James

QUIZ 21

1. What is the postcode of Albert Square?
2. In which county was *Poldark* set?
3. Which role is played by Stan Richards in *Emmerdale*?
4. In which soap set aboard a North Sea ferry did Kate O'Mara play Katherine Laker?
5. Who starred in the action movie *True Lies* before playing the character of Zubin in *Holby City*?
6. Who links the roles of Sable Colby in *Dynasty* and Phyl Oswyn in *Bad Girls*?
7. Who played the title role in *The Duchess Of Duke Street*?
8. Which star of *Auf Wiedersehen Pet*, also played Dr Jack Kerruish in *Peak Practice*?
9. Which blonde bombshell was cast as Amanda Woodward in *Melrose Place*?
10. Which role is played by Ian Smith in *Neighbours*?

ANSWERS

1. E20 2. Cornwall 3. Seth Armstrong 4. *Triangle* 5. Art Malik 6. Stephanie Beacham 7. Gemma Jones 8. Kevin Whately 9. Heather Locklear 10. Harold Bishop

QUIZ 22

Unravel the anagrams to give the titles of TV soaps.

1 ALL SAD
2 LOO DREAD
3 BIG SHOE RUN
4 CANCEL FROST
5 SLAY A CUT
6 HOOK SALLY
7 COPE APLENTY
8 SIR BOOKED
9 BATHE RATE
10 RELATING

ANSWERS

1. *Dallas* 2. *Eldorado* 3. *Neighbours* 4. *Falcon Crest* 5. *Casualty* 6. *Hollyoaks* 7. *Peyton Place* 8. *Brookside* 9. *Heartbeat* 10. *Triangle*

QUIZ 23

1 Which soap celebrated its 1000th episode in June 1990?

2 Who played the role of medical student Neela Rasgotra in *ER*?

3 Who played the role of Suzanne Ross before joining the cast of *EastEnders*?

4 Which actor played Adam in *Cold Feet*?

5 Which series featured a desk sergeant called Bert Lynch?

6 Which actor moved from the Ponderosa to Walnut Grove?

7 Which soap returned to the TV screens in 2001 after a 13-year break?

8 Which radio soap celebrated its 10,000th edition in 1989?

9 Which soap pub is supplied by the Luxford and Copley brewery?

10 What is the name of the nightclub that opened in *EastEnders* in January 2004?

ANSWERS

1. *Emmerdale* 2. Parminder Nagra 3. Sue Tully 4. James Nesbitt 5. *Z Cars* 6. Michael Landon 7. *Crossroads* 8. *The Archers* 9. The Queen Vic 10. The Platform

QUIZ 24

1. Which star of *Coronation Street* was born William Piddington?
2. In which county was the series *Forever Green* set?
3. Which US soap was based on a book penned by Richard and Esther Shapiro?
4. In *EastEnders*, what was the name of the fireman fiancé of Sharon Watts who died shortly before their planned wedding?
5. In *Coronation Street*, what was the name of Minnie Caldwell's cat?
6. What is the name of the fictional football team in *Footballers' Wives*?
7. Which *EastEnders* character appeared on a TV game show called *Cat And Mouse*?
8. Who was revealed as the father of Tracy Barlow's child in January 2004?
9. On which Spanish costa was *Eldorado* set?
10. Who played the role of Miss Diane in *Crossroads*?

ANSWERS

1. Bill Tarmey 2. Gloucestershire 3. *Dynasty* 4. Tom Banks 5. Bobby
6. Earls Park 7. Arthur Fowler 8. Steve McDonald 9. Costa Del Sol
10. Susan Hanson

QUIZ 25

1. Which soap was set at Alfred Memorial Hospital?
2. Which series featured the character of Dr Beth Glover?
3. What is the name of the hospital in *St Elsewhere*?
4. Who played Nurse Carole Young in *Emergency Ward 10*?
5. Which series was based on the stories of A.J Cronin?
6. Who played the title role in *Marcus Welby MD*?
7. In which US state was *Dr Quinn Medicine Woman* set?
8. Who played Dr Mark Greene in *ER*?
9. Which series was set at Henry Park Hospital?
10. In which soap did David Garth play Dr Matthew Armstrong?

ANSWERS

1. *The Young Doctors* 2. *Peak Practice* 3. St Eligius 4. Jill Browne 5. *Dr Finlay's Casebook* 6. Robert Young 7. Colorado 8. Anthony Edwards 9. *Medics* 10. *General Hospital*

QUIZ 26

1 Which TV series featured an oil company called Mogul?

2 In which series did *EastEnders* star Michelle Collins play a holiday rep called Vicky?

3 In *Family Affairs* where did Yasmin and Marc enjoy their honeymoon?

4 Who played Emma Jackson in *Home And Away* before launching her pop career?

5 In which state was the 1980s soap *Flamingo Road* set?

6 Who played a bingo caller in *Coronation Street* and a dustinbinman in *Common As Muck*?

7 In which medical drama does Martin Shaw play Dr Kingsford?

8 In which fictional town is *All Creatures Great And Small* set?

9 Which *Coronation Street* star played the mother of Billy Caspar in the critically acclaimed film *Kes*?

10 Who played Thomas in *Upstairs Downstairs*?

ANSWERS

1. *The Troubleshooters* 2. *Sunburn* 3. The Maldives 4. Dannii Minogue 5. Florida 6. Tim Healy 7. *A & E* 8. Darrowby 9. Lynne Perrie 10. John Alderton

QUIZ 27

1 Who first appeared in *Coronation Street* playing a nurse called Wendy Farmer?

2 What is the name of the hospital in the TV soap *The Royal*?

3 Which former East End barrow boy went on to play PC Gabriel Kent in *The Bill*?

4 Which Icelandic pop star did Vicky Entwistle of *Coronation Street* impersonate on *Stars In Their Eyes*?

5 In 2003, *MIT*, a spin off from *The Bill* began. What do the initials *MIT* stand for?

6 Which soap celebrated its 2000th edition in 1995 with an extended show?

7 Who is the longest-serving male character in *Coronation Street*?

8 Who is the longest-serving female character in *Coronation Street*?

9 In February 1980, which character left *Coronation Street* for Lytham St Annes?

10 Which actress left the *Crossroads* Motel after appearing in 3521 episodes of the show?

ANSWERS

1. Sarah Lancashire 2. St Aidans 3. Todd Carty 4. Bjork 5. Murder Investigation Team 6. *Emmerdale* 7. Ken Barlow 8. Emily Bishop 9. Ena Sharples 10. Noele Gordon

QUIZ 28

What were the maiden names of the following soap characters?

1 Karen Mackenzie in *Knots Landing*
2 Chloe Fraser in *Home And Away*
3 Alma Sedgewick in *Coronation Street*
4 Melanie Mangel in *Neigbours*
5 Miss Ellie Ewing in *Dallas*
6 Jill Osborne in *Hollyoaks*
7 Diane Hunter in *Crossroads*
8 Kim Tate in *Emmerdale*
9 Maxine Peacock in *Coronation Street*
10 Tiffany Mitchell in *EastEnders*

ANSWERS

1. Fairgate 2. Richards 3. Halliwell 4. Pearson 5. Southworth 6. Patrick 7. Lawton 8. Barker 9. Heavey 10. Raymond

QUIZ 29

1. Which soap was screened in Canada under the title of *Caged Women*?
2. Who played the role of Ray Langton in *Coronation Street*?
3. In which soap did David Hargreaves play a market inspector called Derek Owen?
4. Who played Fleur Forsyte in *The Forsyte Saga*?
5. Which former *Coronation Street* star plays Chrissie Williams in *Holby City*?
6. Which husband-to-be of Bet Lynch died in November 2003?
7. What is the last name of Ollie, Marc, Sean and Angie in *Emmerdale*?
8. Which character from *Casualty*, played by Catherine Shipton, is nicknamed Duffy?
9. In which year was *LA Law* screened for the first time on British TV?
10. In which series set in Ireland did Don Wycherley play Father Aidan?

ANSWERS

1. *Prisoner Cell Block H* 2. Neville Buswell 3. *Albion Market* 4. Susan Hampshire 5. Tina Hobley 6. Cecil Newton 7. Reynolds 8. Lisa Duffin 9. 1986 10. *Ballykissangel*

QUIZ 30

1. Which *Coronation Street* actor was once severely criticized for labelling women golfers as 'cockroaches'?
2. What is the name of the motor accessories shop in *Hollyoaks*?
3. In which US soap did the character of Hillary Michaels own an agency called Models Inc?
4. Who first appeared in *Coronation Street* playing a landlady called Mrs Webb?
5. In *Coronation Street* whose baby was dangled from a church roof in 2003?
6. What is the title of the medical series in which Michael French and James Bolam play father and son doctors?
7. Which future Spice Girl played a teenage mugger in *EastEnders*?
8. In which war was *The Sullivans* set?
9. What was Linda's maiden name before she married Mike Baldwin in *Coronation Street*?
10. What is the name of the Kent village in which *The Darling Buds Of May* is set?

ANSWERS

1. Johnny Briggs 2. Dan's Pit Stop 3. *Melrose Place* 4. Jean Alexander 5. Sarah Louise Platt's baby 6. *Born And Bred* 7. Emma Bunton 8. World War II 9. Sykes 10. Pluckley

QUIZ 31

Which soaps are set in the following fictional places?

1 Summer Bay

2 Beckindale

3 Tarrant

4 Cooper's Crossing

5 Newtown

6 Tannochbrae

7 Weatherfield

8 Aidensfield

9 Glendarroch

10 Walford

ANSWERS

1. *Home And Away* 2. *Emmerdale* 3. *Howard's Way* 4. *The Flying Doctors* 5. *Z Cars* 6. *Dr Finlay's Casebook* 7. *Coronation Street* 8. *Heartbeat* 9. *Take The High Road* 10. *EastEnders*

QUIZ 32

1. What species of snake provided the name of a nightclub in *EastEnders*?
2. Which soap featured a singing cabaret star called Trixie Tucker?
3. Which soap is set in the small town of Capeside near the city of Boston?
4. In which series does Jack Ellis play the evil character of Jim Fenner?
5. Which alcoholic spirit was the favourite tipple of Albert Tatlock in the Rover's Return?
6. Who played Nurse Hilda Price in *General Hospital* and went on to star in a series of Oxo TV adverts?
7. In which US state is *ER* set?
8. In the pilot episode of *London's Burning* who played the role of Rambo?
9. Which actor enjoyed a chart hit with the theme song from *Heartbeat*?
10. What was the first name of the oldest son of the Harrington family in *Peyton Place*?

ANSWERS

1. Cobra 2. *Neighbours* 3. *Dawson's Creek* 4. *Bad Girls* 5. Rum 6. Lynda Bellingham 7. Illinois 8. Jerome Flynn 9. Nick Berry 10. Rodney

QUIZ 33

1. In what year did *Holby City* make its TV debut?
2. In which series did Linda Robson and Pauline Quirke play Maggie and Veronica?
3. Which US soap, featuring the character of Kelly Taylor, took its title from a zip code?
4. Derek Wilton and Victor Pendlebury were love rivals for whose hand?
5. Who plays Dr Will Preston in *Peak Practice*?
6. Who played the soap character of Miguel Morez before finding fame as a pop singer?
7. Which series was based on a book entitled *Spencer's Mountain*?
8. Which actor played Reg Holdsworth in *Coronation Street*?
9. In which US city is *The Colby's* set?
10. Who played Ma Larkin in *The Darling Buds Of May*?

ANSWERS

1. 1999 2. *Shine On Harvey Moon* 3. *Beverly Hills 90210* 4. Mavis Riley 5. Simon Shepherd 6. Ricky Martin 7. *The Waltons* 8. Ken Morley 9. Los Angeles 10. Pam Ferris

QUIZ 34

In which cities are or were the following soaps set?

1 *Dynasty*
2 *Hollyoaks*
3 *ER*
4 *Thirtysomething*
5 *When The Boat Comes In*
6 *The Bill*
7 *Neighbours*
8 *St Elsewhere*
9 *Brookside*
10 *Albion Market*

ANSWERS

1. Denver 2. Chester 3. Chicago 4. Philadelphia 5. Newcastle 6. London 7. Melbourne 8. Boston 9. Liverpool 10. Manchester

QUIZ 35

1. Which soap featured a nightclub called La Luz?
2. Who played Tom Howard in *Howard's Way*?
3. What did *Take The High Road* change its title to in 1995?
4. In which soap did Jason Gioberti die in the very first episode?
5. In which US state is *Melrose Place* set?
6. What is the first name of the *Emmerdale* character who has had the surnames of Bates, Merrick, Tate and Glover?
7. Which duo's music was playing on the car stereo, while Derek Wilton was dying from a heart attack?
8. Which future Hollywood star played Betsy Stewart Montgomery Andropoulos in *As The World Turns*?
9. What kind of shop was managed by Miss Tatum in *Crossroads*?
10. Which series featured a boat called the *Charlotte Rose*?

ANSWERS

1. *Brookside* 2. Maurice Colbourne 3. *High Road* 4. *Falcon Crest* 5. California 6. Kathy 7. Gilbert and Sullivan 8. Meg Ryan 9. Post Office 10. *The Onedin Line*

QUIZ 36

1. What is the name of the newsagents in *Coronation Street*?
2. Who played Zachary Powers in *Dynasty* and Khan in the second *Star Trek* movie?
3. What was the name of the sergeant played for many years in *The Bill* by Eric Richard?
4. In *Dallas*, what was the maiden name of Pam Ewing?
5. Who married Bruce Willis after starring as Jackie Templeton in *General Hospital*?
6. Which *Neighbours* character is often heard saying "botheration" when a problem arises?
7. Who played Graham Lodsworth in *Emmerdale* before joining the cast of *EastEnders*?
8. In which US soap does Michael Damian play the role of Danny Romalotti?
9. In which soap mini series did Richard Chamberlain play the amorous Father Ralph?
10. What type of shop does Fred Elliott run in *Coronation Street*?

ANSWERS

1. The Kabin 2. Ricardo Montalban 3. Bob Cryer 4. Barnes 5. Demi Moore 6. Harold Bishop 7. Ross Kemp 8. *The Young And The Restless* 9. *The Thorn Birds* 10. Butcher's shop

QUIZ 37

Unravel the anagrams to give the names of soap opera characters.

1 A BROWN ELK from *Coronation Street*
2 HITCHER RUNS from *Crossroads*
3 SWEET OVEN from *EastEnders*
4 ECHO BEND from *The Bill*
5 TRY BARN RAG from *Brookside*
6 TAKEN RAFT from *Emmerdale*
7 BILLY MOST from *Hollyoaks*
8 BARD SENSE from *Coronation Street*
9 A FINE LOOM from *EastEnders*
10 WANED JEAN from *Dallas*

ANSWERS

1. Ken Barlow 2. Chris Hunter 3. Steve Owen 4. Don Beach 5. Barry Grant 6. Frank Tate 7. Toby Mills 8. Des Barnes 9. Alfie Moon 10. Jenna Wade

QUIZ 38

1. Which soap recorded its 4000th episode in May 2002?
2. In which year was *Coronation Street* extended to three episodes a week?
3. Who has lived in eight different houses in *Coronation Street*?
4. What is the name of the closest town to the village of *Emmerdale*?
5. Which glam rock pop star landed the role of Greg Andersen in *Hollyoaks*?
6. Who played Kendall Hart Lang in *All My Children* before finding fame as a vampire slayer?
7. Who proposed to Sarah Louise Platt in 2004?
8. Which star of the film *The Full Monty* played an ex-convict called Greg Slater in *Brookside*?
9. Which Channel 4 soap features the Freeman family from Liverpool?
10. What is the first name of Deidre's acid-tongued mother in *Coronation Street*?

ANSWERS

1. *Neighbours* 2. 1989 3. Ken Barlow 4. Hotten 5. Alvin Stardust 6. Sarah Michelle Geller 7. Todd Grimshaw 8. Paul Barber 9. *Springhill* 10. Blanche

QUIZ 39

1. Which Weatherfield mum enjoyed an affair with a gangster called Frazer Henderson?
2. In which Yorkshire city was the series *Band Of Gold* set?
3. Who composed the theme for *Crossroads*?
4. In *Coronation Street*, who is the illegitimate son of Les Battersby?
5. In which US soap are the Forrester family the owners of a large fashion company?
6. In *Brookside*, to which city did Mandy Jordache move with her baby Ruth?
7. Who played Dr Mark Toland in *One Life To Live* and went on to don a black suit in the film *Men In Black*?
8. Which US soap featured a dog called Rio?
9. In *Coronation Street* what was Hayley Patterson's name when she was a man?
10. Which US soap featured a newspaper called *The New Globe*?

ANSWERS

1. Liz McDonald 2. Bradford 3. Tony Hatch 4. Greg Kelly 5. *The Bold And The Beautiful* 6. Bristol 7. Tommy Lee Jones 8. *Dynasty* 9. Harold 10. *Falcon Crest*

QUIZ 40

• •

Unravel the anagrams to give the names of actors and actresses from *Coronation Street*.

1 NEXT A HIPPO
2 THORN WHEEL
3 JOB CENSURE
4 WARTY CASH
5 BARON CAN RIP
6 LEERY MONK
7 DRAFT FEES
8 A TRIM BELLY
9 A RIPE LOVING
10 COSTLIER NOVA

ANSWERS

1. Pat Phoenix 2. Helen Worth 3. Bruce Jones 4. Tracy Shaw 5. Brian Capron 6. Ken Morley 7. Fred Feast 8. Bill Tarmey 9. Nigel Pivaro 10. Violet Carson

QUIZ 41

1. Who was the best man of Alf Roberts when he married Audrey?
2. Who played Detective Inspector Bamber in *Z Cars* and went on to play Reggie Perrin?
3. Which *EastEnders* star won the Best Actor Award at the 2003 British Soap Awards?
4. Which soap features a villain called Pete Callan?
5. Who plays Dawson in *Dawson's Creek*?
6. Which actor, from a famous acting family, plays the role of Alex Wells in *Night And Day*?
7. Which soap features a children's playground called the Red Rec?
8. What is the logo of the *Crossroads* Motel?
9. Who played Dr Joshua Hall in *One Life To Live* and went on to star in the *Matrix* films?
10. What is Donald Fisher's job in *Home And Away*?

ANSWERS

1. Mike Baldwin 2. Leonard Rossiter 3. Steve McFadden 4. *Family Affairs* 5. James Van Der Beek 6. Joe McGann 7. *Coronation Street* 8. Three white feathers 9. Laurence Fishburne 10. School headmaster

QUIZ 42

1. Which *Coronation Street* regular lives in Hillside Crescent?
2. Who played twins called Frannie and Sabrina in *As The World Turns* before battling Hannibal Lecter on film?
3. Which long-running radio soap is set in the village of Ambridge?
4. Which former member of Boyzone joined the cast of *Coronation Street* as Ciaran McCarthy?
5. What was the name of the cruise liner in *The Love Boat*?
6. Who played Father Christopher in *Falcon Crest* and also starred as Michael Steadman in *Thirtysomething*?
7. Which actor starred in the police series *City Central* after playing Joe Wicks in *EastEnders*?
8. What was the surname of the character played by Gordon Jackson in *Upstairs Downstairs*?
9. Which organization featured in the series *All Quiet On The Preston Front*?
10. Which star of *Emmerdale* also presented the video clip show *You've Been Framed*?

ANSWERS

1. Betty Williams, formerly Betty Turpin 2. Julianne Moore 3. *The Archers* 4. Keith Duffy 5. *Pacific Princess* 6. Ken Olin 7. Paul Nicholls 8. Hudson 9. The Territorial Army 10. Lisa Riley

QUIZ 43

1. Which *Brookside* character was murdered and buried under a patio?
2. Who played the role of Lindsey Corkhill?
3. What is the surname of the *Brookside* family, who had the first names of Paul, Annabelle, Lucy and Gordon?
4. What was the nickname of Brookside character Thomas Sweeney?
5. Who played the role of Sheila Grant?
6. In what year was the final episode of *Brookside* screened?
7. What was the name of Patricia Farnham's shop?
8. What was *Brookside* originally going to be called?
9. Who played the role of Ron Dixon?
10. On which TV channel was *Brookside* broadcast?

ANSWERS

1. Trevor Jordache 2. Claire Sweeney 3. Collins 4. Sinbad 5. Sue Johnston 6. 2003 7. The Gift Box 8. *Meadowcroft* 9. Vince Earl 10. Channel 4

QUIZ 44

1. Who played Heath in *The Big Valley* before leaping to fame as *The Bionic Man*?
2. Who played the role of Ray Krebbs in *Dallas*?
3. In which radio soap did the main character often say "I'm worried about Jim"?
4. Which series was introduced by a theme music entitled 'Piano Parchment'?
5. What is the name of the Tate's farm in *Emmerdale*?
6. In which English county is *Peak Practice* set?
7. Which *EastEnders* star served a jail sentence in real life for the murder of a taxi driver?
8. Who played the wife of Tom Howard in *Howard's Way*?
9. Is Raul the name of the butler of the Carringtons, the Ewings or the Colbys?
10. Who played Gordon Clegg in *Coronation Street* and went on to become a theatre impressario?

ANSWERS

1. Lee Majors 2. Steve Kanaly 3. *Mrs Dale's Diary* 4. *All Creatures Great And Small* 5. Home Farm 6. Derbyshire 7. Leslie Grantham 8. Jan Harvey 9. The Ewings 10. Bill Kenwright

QUIZ 45

1. In which 1960s soap centred around a magazine did Ronald Allen play a character called Ian Harmon?
2. In which year was Tiffany Mitchell killed in *EastEnders*?
3. Who plays the title role in *Ally McBeal*?
4. What is the character name of *The Duchess Of Duke Street*?
5. In which series did viewers meet a lifeguard called Summer Quinn?
6. What is the first name of the character played by Catherine Zeta Jones in *The Darling Buds Of May*?
7. What was Krystle Carrington's maiden name in *Dynasty*?
8. Which series features a medical practice called Arden House?
9. Who played Ian McKenzie in *A Family At War* and went on to play a Jersey detective?
10. Who portrayed Inspector Jean Darbley in *Juliet Bravo*?

ANSWERS

1. *Compact* 2. 1998 3. Calista Flockhart 4. Louisa Trotter 5. *Baywatch* 6. Mariette 7. Jennings 8. *Dr Finlay's Casebook* 9. John Nettles 10. Stephanie Turner

QUIZ 46

1. Who became known as The Weatherfield One?
2. What is the name of the prison in *Prisoner Cell Block H*?
3. Which soap featured the 'free George Jackson' campaign?
4. In which series did Googie Withers play a prison governess called Faye Boswell?
5. Who played the role of Bea Smith in *Prisoner Cell Block H*?
6. What is the name of the prison in *Bad Girls*?
7. In *Coronation Street* who shared a prison cell with Jed Stone?
8. Which song, a hit for Lynne Hamilton in 1989, was the theme song for *Prisoner Cell Block H*?
9. Who departed from Weatherfield and went on to play a prisoner called Bev Tull in *Bad Girls*?
10. Which character from *Brookside* died from a heart attack while in prison?

ANSWERS

1. Deidre Rachid 2. Wentworth Detention Centre 3. *Brookside* 4. *Within These Walls* 5. Val Lehman 6. Larkhall 7. Eddie Yeats 8. 'On The Inside' 9. Amanda Barrie 10. Beth Jordache

QUIZ 47

1. What is the name of the Texan county where the Ewing family lives?
2. On whose books was *The Little House On The Prairie* based?
3. Which series co-starred former *EastEnders* star Nick Berry and former *Coronation Street* star Tina Hobley?
4. Who played the role of Dr Gillespie in *Dr Kildare*?
5. Who played James Onedin in *The Onedin Line*?
6. In *Northern Exposure*, what was the name of the moose that enjoyed a stroll down the main street?
7. Which children's soap, set in Newcastle, co-starred Ant and Dec?
8. What is the name of the school in *Beverly Hills 90210*?
9. In what type of building did Alexis marry Cecil Colby in *Dynasty*?
10. What breed of dog is Tricki Woo in *All Creatures Great And Small*?

ANSWERS

1. Braddock County 2. Laura Ingalls Wilder 3. *Harbour Lights* 4. Raymond Massey 5. Peter Gilmore 6. Mort 7. *Byker Grove* 8. West Beverly Hills High 9. A hospital 10. Pekinese

QUIZ 48

1. 'An Ordinary Copper' is the title of the theme music for which TV show?
2. Who played Irene in the original series of *The Forsyte Saga*?
3. What is the name of the rival oil company to Ewing Oil, headed by Cliff Barnes?
4. Who did Rita Fairclough marry in *Coronation Street*, despite the fact he was suffering from a terminal illness?
5. In which decade was Ewing Oil founded?
6. Who wrote the novel on which the soap mini series *The Thorn Birds* was based?
7. What is the middle name of Martin Fowler in *EastEnders*?
8. What is the first name of Martin Fowler's mother?
9. Which soap family employed a butler called Henderson?
10. Who played Adam's girlfriend in *Cold Feet* and Ross's girlfriend in *Friends*?

ANSWERS

1. *Dixon Of Dock Green* 2. Nyree Dawn Porter 3. Barnes-Wentworth 4. Ted Sullivan 5. 1930s 6. Colleen McCullogh 7. Albert 8. Pauline 9. The Colbys 10. Helen Baxendale

QUIZ 49

From which TV soaps do the following spin-off shows derive?

1 *Holby City*

2 *Port Charles*

3 *Damon And Debbie*

4 *Pardon The Expression*

5 *The Royal*

6 *The Colbys*

7 *Burnside*

8 *Knot's Landing*

9 *Softly Softly*

10 *Thomas And Sarah*

ANSWERS

1. *Casualty* 2. *General Hospital* 3. *Brookside* 4. *Coronation Street* 5. *Heartbeat* 6. *Dynasty* 7. *The Bill* 8. *Dallas* 9. *Z Cars* 10. *Upstairs Downstairs*

QUIZ 50

1 Which soap theme featured on the Wings album *Venus And Mars*?

2 What is Kevin Webster's job in *Coronation Street*?

3 What was the name of the fictional town, where the series Crown Court was based?

4 Who was the first caretaker of the *Coronation Street* community centre?

5 Who played Dr Michael Rossi in *Peyton Place*?

6 In what decade did *The Archers* make its radio debut?

7 Which 1991 film co-starring Sally Field and Whoopi Goldberg was a send up of TV soaps?

8 Who plays Sally Webster in *Coronation Street*?

9 What is the name of the Waltons' grandfather?

10 Where did Mavis Wilton move to when she left *Coronation Street*?

ANSWERS

1. *Crossroads* 2. Car mechanic 3. Fulchester 4. Ena Sharples 5. Ed Nelson 6. 1950s (1951) 7. *Soapdish* 8. Sally Whitaker 9. Zeb 10. The Lake District

QUIZ 51

1. Who played the character of Jodie Dallas in *Soap* before becoming a major Hollywood star?
2. Who owned the first house in *Coronation Street* to boast an inside toilet?
3. Who played Dr Steve Kiley in *Marcus Welby MD* and went on to marry Barbara Streisand?
4. In *The Sullivans*, what was the first name of Harry Sullivan's first wife?
5. Which character was played by Paul Bradley in *EastEnders*?
6. Which soap character has worked as a cleaner for Mike Baldwin, Annie Walker and Dr Lowther?
7. In the very first episode of *Dallas*, which character was seen in an amorous clinch with Ray Krebbs?
8. For what crime was Meg Richardson given a prison sentence in *Crossroads*?
9. 'Johnny Todd' was the title of the theme music to which series of yesteryear?
10. What disease claimed the life of Alma Baldwin in *Coronation Street*?

ANSWERS

1. Billy Crystal 2. The Barlows 3. James Brolin 4. Rose 5. Nigel Bates 6. Hilda Ogden 7. Lucy Ewing 8. Dangerous driving 9. *Z Cars* 10. Cancer

QUIZ 52

Unravel the anagrams to give the names of ten actors from the soap *EastEnders*.

1 PERK MOSS

2 DOTTY CARD

3 MIDI REEK

4 TRAMPLE A SPY

5 A DEEP RENT

6 COMBATS OP

7 ME TRAP MINK

8 I SNOWED

9 ME A SOLO JOB

10 JERKY CARD

ANSWERS

1. Ross Kemp 2. Todd Carty 3. Mike Reid 4. Patsy Palmer 5. Peter Dean 6. Pat Coombs 7. Martin Kemp 8. Sid Owen 9. Joe Absolom 10. Jack Ryder

QUIZ 53

1. Who played the title role in the medical drama *Ben Casey*?
2. Who drove the car that 'killed' Bobby Ewing?
3. What is the name of Annie Walker's son in *Coronation Street*?
4. What is the name of Annie Walker's daughter in *Coronation Street*?
5. What is the title of the first spin off show from *Baywatch*?
6. Which Weatherfield character is known for his repetitive speech?
7. Which *Crossroads* character died from a heart attack while held hostage by terrorists?
8. In which year did Nick Berry leave the cast of *Heartbeat*?
9. Who played the cook Mrs Bridges in *Upstairs Downstairs*?
10. In which year did *Coronation Street* celebrate its 1000th episode?

ANSWERS

1. Vince Edwards 2. Catherine Wentworth 3. Billy 4. Joan 5. *Baywatch Nights* 6. Fred Elliott 7. Hugh Mortimer 8. 1997 9. Angela Baddeley 10. 1970

QUIZ 54

1. Who plays the role of Sonia Jackson in *EastEnders*?
2. *Conundrum* was the title of the final episode of which US soap?
3. Which former star of the TV series *Minder* went on to play Gary Costello in *Family Affairs*?
4. In which soap did the character of Dan Fixx face a murder charge?
5. Which county did Dolly Skillbeck move to with her son Sam when she left *Emmerdale*?
6. The teen soap *Sweet Valley High* is set in which US state?
7. Who played the role of Prue in the 1970s soap melodrama *A Bouquet Of Barbed Wire*?
8. In the short-lived soap *Triangle*, which English port did the ferry boat travel to and from?
9. In 1976 who became the first winner of the Rear Of The Year Award and went on to star in *EastEnders*?
10. Which show is based on a series of novels entitled *Constable*?

ANSWERS

1. Natalie Cassidy 2. *Dallas* 3. Gary Webster 4. *Falcon Crest* 5. Norfolk 6. California 7. Susan Penhaligon 8. Felixstowe 9. Barbara Windsor 10. *Heartbeat*

QUIZ 55

1. Kate Ford is the fourth actress to play which *Coronation Street* character?
2. In *EastEnders*, who did Todd Carty replace in the role of Mark Fowler?
3. Who, besides Barbara Bel Geddes, played the role of Miss Ellie in *Dallas*?
4. Which role in *Dynasty* was played by both Emma Samms and Pamela Sue Martin?
5. Who has been played on TV by both Robert Wightman and Richard Thomas?
6. Which role in *All Creatures Great And Small* links Carol Drinkwater and Lynda Bellingham?
7. Which *Hollyoaks* role has been shared by Ben Sheriff and Matt Littler?
8. Who replaced Andrew Burt in the *Emmerdale* role of Jack Sugden?
9. Which role in *Dallas* was played by both Keenan Wynn and David Wayne?
10. Whom did Barbara Windsor replace in the Walford role of Peggy Mitchell?

ANSWERS

1. Tracy Barlow 2. David Scarboro 3. Donna Reed 4. Fallon 5. John Boy Walton 6. Helen Herriot 7. Max Cunningham 8. Clive Hornby 9. Digger Barnes 10. Jo Warne

QUIZ 56

1. Which comedian had a cameo role as the wedding chauffeur of Meg Richardson in *Crossroads*?
2. Which actor connects the roles of Jed Stone in *Coronation Street* and Marty Hopkirk in *Randall And Hopkirk Deceased*?
3. What is the name of the character played by David Hasselhoff in *Baywatch*?
4. Which star of *EastEnders* also played a jeweller in the film *Snatch*?
5. Which song, a hit for Anita Dobson, was based on the theme tune of *EastEnders*?
6. In *Coronation Street*, when Deidre married Samir, who gave her a hat to wear at the wedding?
7. Which *Emmerdale* star enjoyed a brief stint in the pop charts with the song 'Just This Side Of Love'?
8. In which year did the character of Arthur Fowler leave *EastEnders*?
9. Who played the role of CJ Lamb in *LA Law*?
10. Which character is nicknamed Tommo in *Peak Practice*?

ANSWERS

1. Larry Grayson 2. Kenneth Cope 3. Mitch Buchannon 4. Mike Reid 5.'Anyone Can Fall In Love' 6. Rita Sullivan 7. Malandra Burrows 8. 1995 9. Amanda Donohoe 10. Alan Tomlins

QUIZ 57

1 Which Spice Girl made a cameo appearance in *Emmerdale* alongside her sister Daniella?

2 Which Weatherfield villain was described as "Norman Bates with a briefcase"?

3 Who played the part of Inspector Monroe in *The Bill*?

4 Which star of *Dynasty* penned an autobiography entitled *Second Act*?

5 The plot of which short-lived soap centred on the occupants of 35 Mafeking Terrace?

6 In *Brookside* what was the name of Nat Simpson's sister with whom he had an incestuous relationship?

7 What is the first name of Dr Finlay's housekeeper, played by Barbara Mullen?

8 In *Dynasty* how did Adam Carrington try to poison Jeff Colby?

9 On whose novels is the series *The Forsyte Saga* based?

10 Which soap features a bistro called Gnosh Village?

ANSWERS

1. Mel B 2. Richard Hillman 3. Colin Tarrant 4. Joan Collins 5. *Rooms* 6. Georgia 7. Janet 8. With poisonous office paint 9. John Galsworthy 10. *Hollyoaks*

QUIZ 58

1. Which medical Australian soap is set in Wandin Valley?
2. In *Home And Away* what is the nearest major city to Summer Bay?
3. In which street is *Neighbours* set?
4. The Palmers and the Hamiltons are the central characters in which Australian soap?
5. What is the link between Craig McLachlan's role in *Home And Away* and Ross Kemp's role in *EastEnders*?
6. Which soap features the characters of Kate Meredith and Flynn Errol?
7. Who played the role of Mike Young in *Neighbours* and went on to become a major movie star?
8. Who composed the theme for *Neighbours*?
9. Tom Callaghan was the lead character in which medical soap?
10. Who played Joe Mangel in *Neighbours*?

ANSWERS

1. *A Country Practice* 2. Sydney 3. Ramsay Street 4. *Sons And Daughters* 5. Both are called Grant Mitchell 6. *The Sullivans* 7. Guy Pearce 8. Tony Hatch 9. *The Flying Doctors* 10. Mark Little

QUIZ 59

1. Which soap featured a dog called Peggy and a horse called Samson?
2. Who played a reluctant stripper in *The Full Monty* before moving to *Coronation Street*?
3. What was the name of the London street that housed the police station in *Dixon Of Dock Green*?
4. Who played Joshua Rush in *Knot's Landing* and went on to marry Kim Basinger?
5. Which author created the fictional town of Darrowby?
6. Who played the role of Assumpta Fitzgerald in *Ballykissangel*?
7. Which soap character left Leonard Swinley standing at the altar?
8. Which character in *Crossroads* was nicknamed Bomber?
9. Which character was played by Nick Berry in *Heartbeat*?
10. Who played the role of Ford Seaton in *When The Boat Comes In*?

ANSWERS

1. *Emmerdale* 2. Bruce Jones 3. Leman Street 4. Alec Baldwin 5. James Herriot 6. Dervla Kirwan 7. Emily Nugent 8. Tommy Lancaster 9. PC Nick Rowan 10. James Bolam

QUIZ 60

1. Robert Foxworth, who starred in *Falcon Crest*, originally turned down which role in *Dallas*?
2. On which chart-topping song did future *EastEnders* star Wendy Richard collaborate with Mike Sarne in the 1960s?
3. Who created Horace Rumpole?
4. Who played Charlene Robinson in *Neighbours*?
5. Which *Coronation Street* star penned an autobiography entitled *The Other Side Of The Street*?
6. In which series did Amanda Redman play the role of Dr Joanna Stevens?
7. In which US soap was a horse called Allegree kidnapped?
8. Which short-lived 1970s soap was set at Larkfield Manor?
9. In which soap did Howard Duff play a character called Titus Semple?
10. Who played the role of CJ Parker in *Baywatch*?

ANSWERS

1. JR Ewing 2. *Come Outside* 3. John Mortimer 4. Kylie Minogue 5. Jean Alexander 6. *Dangerfield* 7. *Dynasty* 8. *The Cedar Tree* 9. *Falcon Crest* 10. Pamela Anderson

QUIZ 61

What is the surname of the following soap families?

1 Sue, Ali and Mehmet in *EastEnders*
2 Tom, Gypsy and Joel in *Home And Away*
3 Bel, Nat and Ollie in *Brookside*
4 Patricia, Frank and Julie in *Knot's Landing*
5 Tommy, Gabriel and Cesar in *Falcon Crest*
6 Les, Toyah and Janice in *Coronation Street*
7 Blair, Gwen and Drew in *Eldorado*
8 Cody, Adam and Doug in *Neigbours*
9 Ashraf, Sufia and Sohail in *EastEnders*
10 Anne, Jack and Billy in *Coronation Street*

ANSWERS

1. Osman 2. Nash 3. Simpson 4. Williams 5. Ortega 6. Battersby 7. Lockhead 8. Willis 9. Karim 10. Walker

QUIZ 62

1. Which actor, who played Bobby Grant in *Brookside*, was jailed in real life for his part in a building workers' strike?
2. In which continent did Jock Ewing die?
3. In which soap did Stella Jones win the lottery?
4. Who played the role of Fiona Middleton in *Coronation Street* before donning a nurse's uniform in *Holby City*?
5. Which rock guitarist did Anita Dobson marry in real life?
6. What were the names of the two central families in the TV series *Soap*?
7. In which soap did Georgina Walker play Jane Harper?
8. In which fictional London suburb is *Family Affairs* set?
9. What was Sam Benson's occupation in *Crossroads*?
10. Who, early in his acting career, played Dr Richard Moon in *Emergency Ward 10*?

ANSWERS

1. Ricky Tomlinson 2. South America 3. *Emmerdale* 4. Angela Griffin 5. Brian May 6. Tates and Campbells 7. *Night And Day* 8. Charnam 9. Newspaper editor 10. John Alderton

QUIZ 63

1 On whose novel was the soap mini series *Lace* based?

2 Which US TV series featured a bar tender called Isaac Washington?

3 What was the maiden name of Sue Ellen in *Dallas*?

4 What did Weatherfield's Leanne Battersby's surname become when she tied the knot with Nick?

5 Who were the first *Coronation Street* residents to install stone cladding on the front of their house?

6 In which fictional county is *The Archers* set?

7 Who played James Bellamy in *Upstairs Downstairs*?

8 What is the title of the Irish soap that is set in the fictional Dublin suburb of Carrigstown?

9 Who played Blake Carrington in the pilot episode of *Dynasty*?

10 What is the first name of the character played by Eric Porter in *The Forsyte Saga*?

ANSWERS

1. Shirley Conran 2. *The Love Boat* 3. Shepard 4. Tilsley 5. The Duckworths 6. Borsetshire 7. Simon Williams 8. *Fair City* 9. George Peppard 10. Soames

QUIZ 64

1. Name the son of the actor Donald Sinden, who played Anthony Mortimer in *Crossroads*?
2. Which actor links the roles of Roy Lambert in *Crossroads* and Max Farnham in *Brookside*?
3. Which star of the film *Gregory's Girl* played Anne-Marie Wade in *Crossroads*?
4. Which stage comedian played the role of Wally Soper?
5. Who played a character called Suzie Samson and went on to become the daughter-in-law of John Major?
6. Which *Crossroads* character was portrayed by Gabriella Drake?
7. Which singer played the role of Holly Brown?
8. What is the name of Meg Richardson's wheelchair bound son?
9. Who played Clifford Leyton and went on to greater fame as a Weatherfield wheeler dealer?
10. From which cruise liner did Meg Richardson wave goodbye to *Crossroads*?

ANSWERS

1. Jeremy Sinden 2. Steven Pinder 3. Dee Hepburn 4. Max Wall 5. Emma Noble 6. Nicola Freeman 7. Stephanie De Sykes 8. Sandy 9. Johnny Briggs 10. *QE 2*

QUIZ 65

1 Which *Dallas* character was resurrected from the dead in a shower?

2 Which family lived at the Ponderosa ranch in *Bonanza*?

3 Who married the daughter of George Dixon in *Dixon Of Dock Green*?

4 What is the first name of Arnie Becker's long-suffering secretary in *LA Law*?

5 What is the name of the local football team in *EastEnders*?

6 In which US series was the general store owned by Ike Godsey?

7 Lou Grant was the editor of which newspaper?

8 On which Lord's estate was Brookside Close built?

9 Was the last episode of *Z Cars* screened in 1977, 1978 or 1979?

10 Which series featured several married couples including Hope and Michael Steadman?

ANSWERS

1. Bobby Ewing 2. The Cartwrights 3. Andy Crawford 4. Roxanne 5. Walford United 6. *The Waltons* 7. *Los Angeles Tribune* 8. Lord Derby 9. 1978 10. *Thirtysomething*

QUIZ 66

1. In the radio soap *Mrs Dale's Diary*, what was Jim Dale's job?
2. The song 'Always There'. a hit for Marti Webb, was the theme for which soap?
3. Which long-running series was based on a play entitled *Woodentop*?
4. In *Crossroads*. what caused the motel to explode in 1967?
5. What is bounded at one end by Rosamund Street and at the other end by Viaduct Street?
6. Which series set in the 1930s and 1940s chronicled the lives of the Ashton family?
7. In which country is *The Far Pavilions* set?
8. Which Nigel replaced Nigel Le Valliant in the medical drama *Dangerfield*?
9. What does the NY stand with regard to *Emmerdale*'s NY Estates?
10. Who played the role of Joyce Harker in the 1960s soap *The Newcomers*?

ANSWERS

1. Doctor 2. *Howard's Way* 3. *The Bill* 4. An unexploded wartime bomb 5. *Coronation Street* 6. *Family At War* 7. India 8. Nigel Havers 9. North Yorkshire 10. Wendy Richard

QUIZ 67

Which Hollywood star played the role of ...

1 Angela Channing in *Falcon Crest*?
2 Jason Colby in *The Colbys*?
3 Daniel Reece in *Dynasty*?
4 Francesca Gioberti in *Falcon Crest*?
5 Clayton Farlowe in *Dallas*?
6 Carter McKay in *Dallas*?
7 Lady Ashley Mitchell in *Dynasty*?
8 Constance Colby in *The Colbys*?
9 Kit Marlowe in *Falcon Crest*?
10 Ruth Galveston in *Knot's Landing*?

ANSWERS

1. Jane Wyman 2. Charlton Heston 3. Rock Hudson 4. Gina Lollobrigida 5. Howard Keel 6. George Kennedy 7. Ali McGraw 8. Barbara Stanwyck 9. Kim Novak 10. Ava Gardner

QUIZ 68

1 What was the surname of the central family in the TV series *The Brothers*?

2 Which Weatherfield character performed under the singing name of Vince St Clair?

3 What is Lucy Ewing's middle name?

4 In which country is the TV soap *Pobol Y Cwn* set?

5 Whose car registrations plate read EWING 3?

6 In which soap did the Robinson's pet dog Basil drown?

7 In *Little House On The Prairie*, what was the name of Laura Ingalls' horse?

8 Which *Casualty* character has had intimate relationships with Baz, Karen, Valerie and Trisha?

9 At the 2003 British Soap Awards who won the award for Sexiest Female?

10 Who turned up on the doorstep of No 10 Brookside Close after leaving her husband Gary?

ANSWERS

1. Hammond 2. Jack Duckworth 3. Ann 4. Wales 5. JR Ewing 6. *Neighbours* 7. Bunny 8. Charlie Fairhead 9. Jessie Wallace 10. Lindsey Corkhill

QUIZ 69

1. In which country is the medical soap *Shortland Street* set?
2. Which *Brookside* couple fell to their death from the scaffolding of Brookside Parade?
3. What is Lou Beale's middle name in *EastEnders*?
4. In Dallas, how did the mother of Cliff Barnes die?
5. Who plays PC Tony Stamp in *The Bill*?
6. In which soap did Betty Ford appear as herself in 1983?
7. Who plays a character called Archie Shuttleworth in *Coronation Street*?
8. Which *Crossroads* character went to retrieve a spanner and did not return for six months?
9. What is Ellie short for in the name of Miss Ellie Ewing?
10. In *Coronation Street*, Phyllis Pearce and Olive Clark vied for the affections of which senior citizen?

ANSWERS

1. New Zealand 2. Danny and Sue Sullivan 3. Ada 4. In a plane crash 5. Graham Cole 6. *Dynasty* 7. Roy Hudd 8. Benny Hawkins 9. Eleanor 10. Percy Sugden

QUIZ 70

1. Which doctor was played by Leonard Fenton in *EastEnders*?
2. In which hospital did Dr Kildare work?
3. Who played an assistant of *Dr Who* before joining the cast of *Emmerdale*?
4. Which doctor had an affair with Maxine Peacock in *Coronation Street*?
5. Who played Dr John Rennie in *Emergency Ward 10* and went on to become the landlord of the Woolpack?
6. Who portrayed Dr Nick Toscanni in *Dynasty*?
7. Which Australian soap featured the characters of Dr Piper, Dr Newman, Dr Garcia and Dr Henderson?
8. Ben Hull played Dr Parr in which soap?
9. In which US soap did Cliff Robertson play Dr Michael Ranson?
10. Dr Plimmer works in which Bristol hospital?

ANSWERS

1. Dr Legg 2. Blair General Hospital 3. Frazer Hines 4. Dr Matt Ramsden 5. Richard Thorpe 6. James Farentino 7. *The Young Doctors* 8. *Brookside* 9. *Falcon Crest* 10. Holby City Hospital

QUIZ 71

1. Who portrayed the character of Inspector Burnside in *The Bill*?
2. In which county is *Howard's Way* set?
3. Who played PC Graham in *Z Cars* and went on to win a Best Screenplay Oscar for *Chariots Of Fire*?
4. At what number of *Coronation Street* is the corner shop?
5. Which member of the Ewing family owned a ranch called Cedar Ridge?
6. Which star of the 1960s soap *Compact* went on to play the wife of Gordon Kaye in *Allo Allo*?
7. Which country did Michelle Fowler move to when she left Walford?
8. Which British actor played the father of Blake Carrington in *Dynasty*?
9. Which crime resulted in a court case for Ena Sharples?
10. At the 2003 soap awards which *Coronation Street* star picked up the gong for Best Dramatic Performance?

ANSWERS

1. Christopher Ellison 2. Hampshire 3. Colin Welland 4. 15 5. Bobby Ewing 6. Carmen Silvera 7. USA 8. Harry Andrews 9. Shoplifting 10. Sue Nicholls

QUIZ 72

1. Who played Andy O'Brien in *EastEnders*, the character that met his death while saving a child from the path of a car?
2. Which publican was portrayed by Arthur Pentelow in *Emmerdale Farm*?
3. Which Weatherfield villain died from a punctured lung, sustained while he was trying to kill Steve McDonald?
4. By what nickname is Francis Albert Dingle better known?
5. Which member of the Ewing clan was played by Cathy Podewell?
6. Which *Eastender* stole the Christmas Club money to pay for his daughter Michelle's wedding?
7. On whose novels is the TV series *Heartbeat* set?
8. What is the name of the local hospital in *Coronation Street*?
9. In *Home And Away*, what was the three-letter nickname of the character of Peter O'Neale?
10. Which Ewing brother was played by Ted Shackleford?

ANSWERS

1. Ross Davidson 2. Henry Wilks 3. Jez Quigley 4. Butch 5. Cally Harper Ewing 6. Arthur Fowler 7. Nicholas Rhea 8. Weatherfield General 9. Tug 10. Gary Ewing

QUIZ 73

In *Coronation Street* who played ...

1 PC Wilcox and went on to star in the sitcoms, *Porridge* and *Rising Damp*?

2 Bernard Butler and went on to star in the sitcom *Allo, Allo*?

3 Stanley Fairclough and went on to front the pop group Herman's Hermits?

4 Leonard Swindley and went on to play Captain Mainwaring?

5 Dr Graham and went on to play a prison warder in *Porridge*?

6 The grandson of Ena Sharples before joining The Monkees?

7 Detective Sergeant Cross and went on to play a big game hunter in *Jurassic Park: The Lost World*?

8 Ron Jenkins and went on to become an Oscar-winnning actor?

9 Eileen Hughes and went on to play Sybil Fawlty?

10 Malcolm Nuttall and went on to become a leading stage musical star?

ANSWERS

1. Richard Beckinsale 2. Gordon Kaye 3. Peter Noone 4. Arthur Lowe 5. Fulton Mackay 6. Davey Jones 7. Pete Postlethwaite 8. Ben Kingsley 9. Prunella Scales 10. Michael Ball

QUIZ 74

1. From which US state did the Walsh family move to California in the soap *Beverly Hills 90210*?
2. In *Neighbours* what did Beth Brennan's surname become when she married Brad?
3. Which *Dr Who* actor played George Barton in *Coronation Street*?
4. In *Brookside*, what is the family surname of Joey, Niamh, Matt, Kelly and Luke?
5. Which role was played by Craig Fairbrass in *EastEnders*?
6. What is the first name of Dr Plimmer in *Casualty*?
7. Did *The Bill* celebrate its 1000th episode in 1995, 1996 or 1997?
8. In *Coronation Street* was Rosie Webster born in 1988, 1989 or 1990?
9. What is the name of the home estate of the Colbys?
10. Which former landlord of The Woolpack was famed for his mutton chop sideburns?

ANSWERS

1. Minnesota 2. Willis 3. Patrick Troughton 4. Musgrove 5. Dan Sullivan 6. Ewart 7. 1996 8. 1990 9. Belvedere 10. Amos Brearley

QUIZ 75

1. In *Coronation Street* in which year did Jack Duckworth qualify for his old age pension?
2. In which decade is *Heartbeat* set?
3. In *The Bill* what is the first name of PC Hollis?
4. How many John Ross Ewings are there in *Dallas*?
5. What is the name of Terry and Lisa Duckworth's son?
6. Which Walford wide boy killed his girlfriend Saskia?
7. Who played Phyllis Pearce in *Coronation Street*?
8. What is the family surname of the Walford characters of Nicky, Rosa and Gianni?
9. What was the medical specialty of Dr Ross in *ER*?
10. In *Coronation Street* what was the first name of the wife of Eddie Yeats?

ANSWERS

1. 2000 2. 1960s 3. Reg 4. Three 5. Tommy 6. Steve Owen 7. Jill Summers 8. Di Marco 9. Paediatrics 10. Marion

QUIZ 76

Unravel the anagrams to give the names of soap characters.

1 WREN JIG in *Dallas*
2 ADD LYING MEN in *Emmerdale*
3 HOT LEG VERB in *Peak Practice*
4 HITS BEAM in *Prisoner Cell Block H*
5 FLIP PERT PEACH in *Home And Away*
6 ZETA TOE in *Emmerdale*
7 A GREY WING in *Dallas*
8 A LICE GLORY in *Coronation Street*
9 COLONY JABS in *The Colbys*
10 A RENTAL RUN in *Emmerdale*

ANSWERS

1. JR Ewing 2. Mandy Dingle 3. Beth Glover 4. Bea Smith 5. Pippa Fletcher 6. Zoe Tate 7. Gary Ewing 8. Alec Gilroy 9. Jason Colby 10. Alan Turner

QUIZ 77

1. Which member of the British royal family made a guest appearance on *The Archers*?
2. Which *Brookside* character committed suicide by throwing herself off the Mersey ferry?
3. Who played the role of Donna Martin in *Beverly Hills 90210*?
4. Who wrote the lyrics for the theme to *Neighbours*?
5. Which soap featured a taxi firm called Oz Cabs?
6. In which soap did Pauline Quirke and Fiona Fullerton play student nurses?
7. Which character, portrayed by Mary Crosby, shot JR Ewing?
8. Amy Burton is the mother of which *Coronation Street* character?
9. In which city was the Australian soap *The Sullivans* set?
10. What type of shop is located at No 2 Coronation Street?

ANSWERS

1. Princess Margaret 2. Diane Murray (played by Bernadette Nolan) 3. Tori Spelling 4. Jackie Trent 5. *EastEnders* 6. *Angels* 7. Kristin Shepard 8. Vera Duckworth 9. Melbourne 10. Hairdresser's

QUIZ 78

1. Which is Britain's longest-running soap opera?
2. 'Barwick Green' is the title of the theme music for which soap?
3. What was Kim Tate's horse called, that perished in the *Emmerdale* plane crash?
4. Who played Clifford Leyton in *Crossroads* before joining the cast of *Coronation Street*?
5. What is the first name of the *Dynasty* character Dex Dexter?
6. Who owned a donkey called Jenny in *Emmerdale*?
7. Which *Coronation Street* character fell pregnant at 12 years of age?
8. In *Crossroads* who attempted to poison Meg Mortimer, in an attempt to cash in on an insurance policy?
9. Who links the roles of Mickey Malone in *Coronation Street* and the comedy creation Selwyn Froggitt?
10. Which Weatherfield couple remarried in a Manchester prison in 2000?

ANSWERS

1. *Coronation Street* 2. *The Archers* 3. Dark Star 4. Johnny Briggs 5. Farnsworth 6. Seth Armstrong 7. Sarah Louise Platt 8. Malcolm Ryder 9. Bill Maynard 10. Jim and Liz McDonald

QUIZ 79

In which years were the following soaps first screened on British television?

1 *Brookside*
2 *EastEnders*
3 *Emmerdale Farm*
4 *Eldorado*
5 *Coronation Street*
6 *Crossroads*
7 *The Bill*
8 *General Hospital*
9 *Hollyoaks*
10 *Casualty*

ANSWERS

1 1982 2. 1985 3. 1972 4. 1992 5. 1960 6. 1964 7. 1983 8. 1972 9. 1995 10. 1986

QUIZ 80

1. Which was Britian's first twice-weekly soap opera?
2. In which Australian state is *Home And Away* set?
3. Gavin Taylor was the first character to die in which soap?
4. Which series featured a newspaper called *The Blue Ridge Chronicle*?
5. What is the name of Ashley and Maxine Peacock's son in *Coronation Street*?
6. Which character died at the same time as Ashley and Maxine Peacock's wedding?
7. Martin Kemp of *EastEnders* was once a member of which new romantic pop group?
8. Which soap was originally titled *The Vintage Years*?
9. Amy Turtle worked as a cleaner at which soap venue?
10. On which Weatherfield street is Roy Cropper's café to be found?

ANSWERS

1. *Emergency Ward 10* 2. New South Wales 3. *Brookside* 4. *The Waltons* 5. Joshua 6. Judy Mallett 7. Spandau Ballet 8. *Falcon Crest* 9. *Crossroads* Motel 10. Victoria Street

QUIZ 81

1. What is the middle name of Tracy Barlow in *Coronation Street*?
2. Which 1960s soap was set in the town of Angleton?
3. Who played the daughter of George Dixon in *Dixon Of Dock Green* and the mother of the Kray twins on film?
4. Which Weatherfield baby was born on the sofa at No 7 Coronation Street in December 2001?
5. What is the London address of the Bellamys in *Upstairs Downstairs*?
6. What type of bird was Rover in *The Waltons*?
7. Which fellow employee of The Rovers Return often referred to Jack Duckworth as "Duck egg"?
8. On which TV channel was *Family Affairs* launched in 1997?
9. Who played Samantha Failsworth in *Coronation Street* and went on to play Chrissie Williams in *Holby City*?
10. Who links the roles of Mrs Snape in *Coronation Street* and Mrs Bucket in a popular sitcom?

ANSWERS

1. Lynette 2. *The Newcomers* 3. Billie Whitelaw 4. Ben Watts, son of Curly 5. 165 Eaton Place 6. Peacock 7. Bet Lynch 8. Channel 5 9. Tina Hobley 10. Patricia Routledge

QUIZ 82

Name the actors, all of whom have the first name Michael, that played the following soap opera characters.

1. Ollie Simpson in *Brookside*
2. Charles Scott in *Knot's Landing*
3. Kevin Webster in *Coronation Street*
4. Prince Michael in *Dynasty*
5. J Henry Pollard in *Crossroads*
6. Jamie Hart in *Family Affairs*
7. David Wicks in *EastEnders*
8. Beppe Di Marco in *EastEnders*
9. Eddie Royle in *EastEnders*
10. Harry Slater in *EastEnders*

ANSWERS

1. Michael J Jackson 2. Michael York 3. Michael Le Vell 4. Michael Praed 5. Michael Turner 6. Michael Cole 7. Michael French 8. Michael Greco 9. Michael Melia 10. Michael Elphick

QUIZ 83

1. Which actor, and father-in-law of Tony Blair, played the role of Ted Pilkington in *Albion Market*?
2. Which actor plays Oscar Blaketon in *Heartbeat*?
3. The singer Jane McDonald found fame after appearing in which docu-soap?
4. What is the first name of the soap character whose surnames have been Morrell, Carrington, Colby, Dexter and Rowan?
5. Who played Leanne Battersby in *Coronation Street* and PC Gemma Osbourne in *The Bill*?
6. How is Dallas star Mary Crosby related to the legendary crooner Bing Crosby?
7. What was the name of the ferry company in the short-lived soap *Triangle*?
8. What was the nickname of the character in *Grange Hill* played by Todd Carty?
9. Who is the famous acting sister of former *EastEnders* star Nadia Sawalha?
10. Paul O'Grady and Cliff Richard have both appeared in which soap pub as extras?

ANSWERS

1. Anthony Booth 2. Derek Fowlds 3. *The Cruise* 4. Alexis (in *Dynasty*) 5. Jane Danson 6. Father and daughter 7. Triangle Lines 8. Tucker 9. Julia Sawalha 10. The Rovers Return

QUIZ 84

1. Name the cousin of Paul McCartney who starred as Kate Loring in *Crossroads*.
2. *Coronation Street* star Sue Nicholls is married to which former *Street* star in real life?
3. Who played the title role in *Ally McBeal*?
4. In which Irish county is *Ballykissangel* set?
5. Which TV producer has been responsible for shows such as *Dynasty*, *Charlie's Angels* and *Beverly Hills 90210*?
6. In which century was the TV series *The Borgias* set?
7. Who was visited by an angel in the final episode of *Dallas*?
8. In which country is *The District Nurse* set?
9. Who landed the role of Dr Thomas Owen in the BBC soap *The Doctors*?
10. Which bronzed actor played the role of Joel Abigore in *Dynasty*?

ANSWERS

1. Kate Robbins 2. Mark Eden 3. Calista Flockhart 4. County Wicklow 5. Aaron Spelling 6. 15th century 7. JR Ewing 8. Wales 9. Nigel Stock 10. George Hamilton

QUIZ 85

1. Who landed her role in *Dynasty* after her steamy performance in the film *The Bitch*?
2. Who did James Callaghan once describe as "the sexiest woman on TV"?
3. Which screen vamp has had roles in *Howard's Way*, *Triangle*, *Dynasty* and *Crossroads*?
4. Who played the Weatherfield car mechanic Chris Collins?
5. Which heart throb played the role of Dylan McKay in *Beverly Hills 90210*?
6. Which blonde bombshell played the character of Lucy Ewing?
7. Which iconic film goddess played Jacqueline Perrault in *Falcon Crest*?
8. Which *Coronation Street* star had a 1999 top ten chart hit with the song 'I Breathe Again'?
9. Which *Hollyoaks* hunk is played by Alex Carter?
10. Who was voted Sexiest Male Actor at the 2003 British Soap Awards?

ANSWERS

1. Joan Collins 2. Pat Phoenix 3. Kate O'Mara 4. Matthew Marsden 5. Luke Perry 6. Charlene Tilton 7. Lana Turner 8. Adam Rickitt 9. Lee Hunter 10. Shane Richie

QUIZ 86

1. What was the name of Sebastian Flyte's teddy bear in *Brideshead Revisited*?
2. Which classic show ended each episode with the lead character whistling the tune 'Maybe It's Because I'm A Londoner'?
3. Who played the role of Ronald Merrick in *Jewel In The Crown*?
4. In *Little House On The Prairie*, who portrayed Laura Ingalls?
5. On whose novel was the soap mini series *The Mallens* set?
6. Who played the title role in the football soap *The Manageress*?
7. Which medical soap was originally going to be entitled *Calling Nurse Roberts*?
8. Who played the mother of Heather Locklear in *Melrose Place*?
9. Who played a nurse in *Marcus Welby MD* before finding greater fame in the Emmy-winning show *Cagney & Lacey*?
10. Which actor played the title role in *Lou Grant*?

ANSWERS

1. Aloysius 2. *Dixon Of Dock Green* 3. Tim Piggott-Smith 4. Melissa Gilbert 5. Catherine Cookson 6. Cherie Lunghi 7. *Emergency Ward 10* 8. Linda Gray 9. Sharon Gless 10. Ed Asner

QUIZ 87

1. In which series does Linda Henry play a fearsome prison inmate called Yvonne Atkins?
2. To which country did Nick Tilsley move, to live with his uncle when he left Weatherfield?
3. Which series featured a Glaswegian badger-keeping vet called Calum Buchanan?
4. Which soap character worked as a car salesman for Knot's Landing Motors?
5. Under what name did *Byker Grove* stars Ant and Dec enjoy pop chart success?
6. Who, early in his acting career, played a squatter in *Coronation Street* and went on to star in *The Professionals*?
7. Who played Pop Larkin in *The Darling Buds Of May*?
8. Which series featured the characters of PC Danny Spark, Sergeant Joe Beck and Inspector Kate Longton?
9. In which series did the actor Kenneth More play a character called Jolyon?
10. Which character in *LA Law* fell to her death down an empty lift shaft?

ANSWERS

1. *Bad Girls* 2. Canada 3. *All Creatures Great And Small* 4. Gary Ewing 5. PJ and Duncan 6. Martin Shaw 7. David Jason 8. *Juliet Bravo* 9. *The Forsyte Saga* 10. Roz Shays

QUIZ 88

In *Coronation Street* who played …

1. Alec Gilroy, the husband of Bet?
2. Alf Roberts, the husband of Audrey?
3. Martin Platt, the ex-husband of Gail?
4. Gary Mallett, the husband of Judy?
5. Samir Rachid, the husband of Deidre?

In *EastEnders* who played…

6. Sue Osman, the wife of Ali?
7. Kathy Beale, the ex-wife of Pete?
8. The first wife of Grant Mitchell?
9. Bianca Butcher, the wife of Ricky?
10. Kat Moon, the wife of Alfie?

ANSWERS

1. Roy Barraclough 2. Brian Mosley 3. Sean Wilson 4. Ian Mercer 5. Al Nedjari 6. Sandy Ratcliff 7. Gillian Taylforth 8. Letitia Dean 9. Patsy Palmer 10. Jessie Wallace

QUIZ 89

1 In which award-winning US series did Tom Skerritt play Sheriff Jimmy Brock?

2 Which Australian production company is responsible for *Neighbours*?

3 Which medical series features the characters of Dr Nyland, Dr Shutt and Dr Kronk?

4 Which was the home city of the Onedins in *The Onedin Line*?

5 Who portrayed Constance McKenzie in the 1960s soap *Peyton Place*?

6 In which soap did Sir John and Lady Margareta Ross-Gifford become tennants of Glendarroch House?

7 Which Dutch port did the ferry boat travel to in *Triangle*?

8 Which star of *The Sound Of Music* played Archbishop Contini-Verchese in *The Thorn Birds*?

9 In which decade was *When The Boat Comes In* set?

10 In the 1960s football soap *United*, what was the name of the United football team?

ANSWERS

1. *Picket Fences* 2. Grundy Television Productions 3. *Chicago Hope* 4. Liverpool 5. Dorothy Malone 6. *High Road* 7. Rotterdam 8. Christopher Plummer 9. 1920s 10. Brentwich United

QUIZ 90

1 In which US state was *The Big Valley* set?

2 Who played Maria Cooper in the 1960s soap *The Newcomers*?

3 Which medical examiner, portrayed by Jack Klugman, was often seen drinking in Danny's Place?

4 Which Australian soap introduced the characters of Andy Green, Charlie Bartlett and David Palmer?

5 Which short-lived US soap, set in the state of Georgia, featured the characters of Peyton Richards and Travis Peterson?

6 Who played Jessica Tate in *Soap*?

7 On whose novel was the series *The Pallisers* set?

8 For what crime was Franky Doyle imprisoned in *Prisoner Cell Block H*?

9 'The Lightning Tree' was the theme song for which 1970s children's soap, adapted from the novel *Cobbler's Dream*?

10 During which war was *The Monocled Mutineer* set?

ANSWERS

1. California 2. Judy Geeson 3. Quincy 4. *Sons And Daughters* 5. *Savannah* 6. Katherine Helmond 7. Anthony Trollope 8. Armed robbery 9. *Follyfoot* 10. World War I

QUIZ 91

Which soap star had a hit with the song…

1 'Tears On My Pillow' in 1990?
2 'Perfect Moment' in 1999?
3 'Every Loser Wins' in 1986?
4 'Don't It Make You Feel Good' in 1989?
5 'Kiss Kiss' in 2002?
6 'Someone To Love' in 1994?
7 'This Is It' in 1993?
8 'Sweetness' in 1994?
9 'Torn' in 1997?
10 'Mona' in 1990?

ANSWERS

1. Kylie Minogue 2. Martine McCutcheon 3. Nick Berry 4. Stefan Dennis 5. Holly Valance 6. Sean McGuire 7. Dannii Minogue 8. Michelle Gayle 9. Natalie Imbruglia 10. Craig McLachlan

QUIZ 92

1. In *The Archers*, how was Tom Archer killed?
2. In *Emmerdale*, which organ did the daughter of Elizabeth Grainger receive from Tricia?
3. In which 1960s series did Johnny Briggs play Detective Sergeant Russell?
4. Which role is played by Leah Bracknell in *Emmerdale*?
5. Which *Eastender* married former Hear'Say member Kym Marsh in real life?
6. Who played Laurence Kirbridge in *Upstairs Downstairs* and went on to play *The Saint*?
7. Which prime minister was portrayed by Howard Lang in the soap mini series *The Winds Of War*?
8. Who plays the role of Carrie in *Sex And The City*?
9. What do the Fowlers sell on their Albert Square market stall?
10. Which short-lived soap was set in a public house called The Mulberry?

ANSWERS

1. Crushed by a tractor 2. Heart 3. *No Hiding Place* 4. Zoe Tate 5. Jack Ryder 6. Ian Ogilvy 7. Winston Churchill 8. Sarah Jessica Parker 9. Fruit and vegetables 10. *World's End*

QUIZ 93

1. Who appeared topless in the opening episode of *Triangle*?
2. On which radio station is *The Archers* broadcast?
3. In which series did *EastEnders* star Leslie Grantham play Danny Kane?
4. Which role was played by Robert Hardy in *All Creatures Great And Small*?
5. In *The Darling Buds Of May*, what did Mariette Larkin's surname become when she married Cedric?
6. Which actor played the role of President Bartlet in *The West Wing*?
7. Who played Kim Tate in *Emmerdale*?
8. Which series was a spin off from the TV film *Panic At Malibu Beach*?
9. Which knighted Oscar winner played Lord Marchmain in *Brideshead Revisited*?
10. Who played the role of Caroline Ingalls in *The Little House On The Prairie*?

ANSWERS

1. Kate O'Mara 2. Radio 4 3. *The Paradise Club* 4. Siegfried Farnon 5. Charlton 6. Martin Sheen 7. Claire King 8. *Baywatch* 9. Sir Laurence Olivier 10. Karen Grassle

QUIZ 94

Identify the soaps from each group of three cast characters.

1 Brian Drake, Dawn Cunnigham and Jodie Nash
2 Steve Loxton, Ruby Buxton and Nick Klein
3 Shelley Sutherland, Floss McPhee and Damian Roberts
4 Roxanne Bird, Mel Dyson and Clive King
5 Jeannie Brooks, Lynn Warner and Franky Doyle
6 Rebecca Dawson, WPC Benson and Bob Massey
7 Paula Vertosick, Betsy Gibson and Jason Avery
8 Nikki Witt, Ryan Saunders and Joe Bradley
9 Robbie McGovern, Ernest O'Keefe and Christopher Merchant
10 Laura McKenzie, Colin Parrish and Sandra Hallam

ANSWERS

1. *Hollyoaks* 2. *The Bill* 3. *Home And Away* 4. *Casualty* 5. *Prisoner Cell Block H* 6. *Peak Practice* 7. *Knot's Landing* 8. *Beverly Hills 90210* 9. *The Sullivans* 10. *London's Burning*

QUIZ 95

1. On whose novel was the series *A Bouquet Of Barbed Wire* based?
2. Which *Brookside* character threatened to commit suicide after it was revealed he was not a qualified teacher?
3. Who played the title role in the 1980s rag trade soap *Connie*?
4. Which character was introduced into *Dynasty* as a surprise witness in a court case involving her ex-husband Blake?
5. What is the first name of Mrs Bridges in *Upstairs Downstairs*?
6. What was Tom Cadman's army rank in *Soldier Soldier*?
7. Who links the roles of Bernice Blackstock in *Emmerdale* and Sally Boothe in *Where The Heart Is*?
8. Which stars of *EastEnders* duetted on the 1986 hit record 'Something Outta Nothing'?
9. Which radio soap featured a milkman called Sydney?
10. On whose novel was the soap mini series *Rich Man Poor Man* based?

ANSWERS

1. Andrea Newman 2. Jimmy Corkhill 3. Stephanie Beacham 4. Alexis 5. Kate 6. Major 7. Samantha Giles 8. Letitia Dean and Paul Medford 9. *Mrs Dale's Diary* 10. Irwin Shaw

QUIZ 96

1. In which series did Nick Berry play Lieutenant Commander Mike Nicholls?
2. What nickname was bestowed upon PC Tony Smith in *The Bill*?
3. In which soap does David Easter play a villain called Pete Callan?
4. Which builder is played by Bill Ward in *Coronation Street*?
5. Which soap spin off features the characters of Jill Weatherill and Dr Ormerod?
6. In *Home And Away*, who rekindled her romance with Dylan Russell after discovering he was not her half brother?
7. In *Hollyoaks*, who came to blows with Abby Hunter after confessing to an affair with Lee Hunter?
8. Who played a transvestite called Roxanne in *The Bill* and went on to create the comic character of Lily Savage?
9. In which soap was Ronny Ferreira hospitalized following a stabbing incident in 2004?
10. Which well-known actress played the role of Lillian Spencer in *Coronation Street*?

ANSWERS

1. *Harbour Lights* 2. Yorkie 3. *Family Affairs* 4. Charlie Stubbs 5. *The Royle* 6. Kirsty Sutherland 7. Zara Morgan 8. Paul O'Grady 9. *EastEnders* 10. Maureen Lipman

QUIZ 97

Identify the soap opera from each group of three cast characters.

1. Mavis Hooper, Archie Gibbs and Rosemary Hunter
2. Zoe Davis, Danny Stark and Doug Willis
3. Mitch Cooper, Mandy Winger and Dusty Farlow
4. Michelle Dockley, Denny Blood and Snowball Merriman
5. Sister Easby, Patricia Rutherford and Sister Frazer
6. Debbie Wilkins, Dr Fonseca and Zoe Slater
7. Matthew Swain, Norman Harrington and Ada Jacks
8. Roy Glover, Eric Pollard and Syd Woolfe
9. Holly Hart, Albie Leach and Yasmin Matthews
10. Joy Slater, Stanley Webb and Trish Valentine

ANSWERS

1. *Crossroads* 2. *Neighbours* 3. *Dallas* 4. *Bad Girls* 5. *Angels* 6. *EastEnders* 7. *Peyton Place* 8. *Emmerdale* 9. *Family Affairs* 10. *Eldorado*

QUIZ 98

1. In which series did Gavin MacLeod play Captain Stubing?
2. Also the name of a world famous comedian, which character was played by Antony Audenshaw in *Emmerdale*?
3. Which character is portrayed by Matt Milburn in *Hollyoaks*?
4. What is the name of the Rovers Return employee played by Iain Rogerson?
5. What is the rank of Gina Gold in *The Bill*?
6. In *Home And Away* who proposed to teacher Sally Fletcher while dressed as a schoolboy?
7. Which president of the USA was portrayed by Ralph Bellamy in the soap mini series *The Winds Of War*?
8. What is the name of Flick Scully's big sister in *Neigbours*?
9. Which *Emmerdale* character, played by Sammy Windward, enjoyed romantic liaisons with Robert and Andy Sugden?
10. What was the first name of the Colby family member played by Claire Yarlett?

ANSWERS

1. *The Love Boat* 2. Bob Hope 3. Joe Spencer 4. Harry Flagg 5. Inspector 6. Flynn Saunders 7. President Franklin D Roosevelt 8. Steph 9. Katie Addyman 10. Bliss

QUIZ 99

1. What was the name of the ferry boat in the TV soap *Triangle*?
2. Which comedian landed the role of Doug Mackenzie in *Family Affairs*?
3. In which series did Derek Jacobi play Lord Fawn?
4. Which series was based on a book entitled *Adventures Of A Black Bag*?
5. In which soap do viewers meet a publican called Lou Carpenter?
6. Who played the role of Barbie Batchelor in *The Jewel In The Crown*?
7. What is the name of Laura Ingalls sister, played in *The Little House On The Prairie* by Melissa Sue Anderson?
8. Who played Ian McKenzie in *A Family At War* and went on to solve crimes on the island of Jersey?
9. Who did Jack Sugden propose to in *Emmerdale* in 2004?
10. In *Coronation Street* what is the family surname of Katy, Tommy, Angela and Craig?

ANSWERS

1. *Tor Scandinavia* 2. Gareth Hale 3. *The Pallisers* 4. *Dr Finlay's Casebook* 5. Neighbours 6. Peggy Ashcroft 7. Mary 8. John Nettles 9. Diane Blackstock 10. Harris

QUIZ 100

Identify the soap from each group of three cast characters.

1. Jasmine Hopkins, Nick Jordan and Jane Archer
2. Dominique Deveraux, Michael Torrance and Jeanette Robins
3. PC Crane, Dr Peters and Bernard Scripps
4. Lisa O'Shea, Roy Harrison and Viv Harker
5. Joey Potter, Abby Morgan and Doug Witter
6. Dr Weaver, Dr Morgenstern and Dr Greene
7. Bill Webster, Jenny Bradley and Audrey Roberts
8. Sandy Wallace, Fergus Jamieson and Brian Blair
9. Sheriff Robins, Tony Cumson and Emma Channing
10. Petra Taylor, Jackie Corkhill and Chrissy Rogers

ANSWERS

1. *Holby City* 2. *Dynasty* 3. *Heartbeat* 4. *Albion Market* 5. *Dawson's Creek* 6. *ER* 7. *Coronation Street* 8. *Take The High Road* 9. *Falcon Crest* 10. *Brookside*

QUIZ 101

1. Which chart-topping singer was *Dynasty* star Joan Collins formerly married to?
2. Who played the role of Des Barnes in *Coronation Street*?
3. Who played Victoria Barkley's daughter Audra in *The Big Valley* and went on to star in *Dynasty*?
4. How did Debbie Bates die in *EastEnders*?
5. What was the first name of Tosh Lines in *The Bill*?
6. At which soap pub has Louise Appleton worked behind the bar?
7. Who played man and wife in *Brookside* and went on to play man and wife in *The Royle Family*?
8. Which *Home And Away* character is the mother of VJ?
9. Who played a prison officer called Barry Pearce in *Bad Girls* and DI Manson in *The Bill*?
10. What is the name of the Walford tube station on the London underground?

ANSWERS

1. Anthony Newley 2. Philip Middlemiss 3. Linda Evans 4. Knocked down by a car 5. Alfred 6. The Woolpack 7. Ricky Tomlinson and Sue Johnston 8. Leah Patterson 9. Andrew Lancel 10. Walford East

QUIZ 102

1. What was the nickname of fireman Geoff Pearce in *London's Burning*?
2. Which *Coronation Street* character died in a convent in 1995?
3. Which character from *Family Affairs* had a one night stand with her stepfather, Pete Callan?
4. Who plays the comic character of Bombhead in *Hollyoaks*?
5. In 2004, which school teacher was murdered in *Home And Away*?
6. In which soap did Toadie get married in 2003?
7. Who played the role of Helen Raven in *Crossroads* and Chastity Dingle in *Emmerdale*?
8. In which series did Jack Davenport play the role of Miles?
9. What is the surname of Izzy, Karl and Susan in *Neighbours*?
10. Which soap doctor was created by Max Brand?

ANSWERS

1. Poison 2. Ivy Brennan 3. Lucy Day 4. Lee Otway 5. Angie Russell 6. *Neighbours* 7. Lucy Pargeter 8. *This Life* 9. Kennedy 10. Dr Kildare

QUIZ 103

Identify each *Coronation Street* bride from the name of the bridegroom and the year of the wedding.

1 2002 Richard Hillman
2 2001 Steve McDonald
3 1998 Des Barnes
4 1997 Fred Elliott
5 1995 Curly Watts
6 1988 Don Brennan
7 1981 Fred Gee
8 1977 Len Fairclough
9 1965 David Barlow
10 1961 Harry Hewitt

ANSWERS

1. Gail Platt 2. Karen Phillips 3. Natalie Horrocks 4. Maureen Holdsworth 5. Raquel Wolstenhulme 6. Ivy Tilsley 7. Eunice Nuttall 8. Rita Littlewood 9. Irma Ogden 10. Concepta Riley

QUIZ 104

1. Which soap hospital employed a receptionist called Susan Deigh?
2. Which series featured the characters of Dr Willard, Sheriff Bridges and Reverend Fordwicke?
3. Which TV show was the brainchild of a former lifeguard called Gregory J Bonaan?
4. Which spiteful character was portrayed by Alison Arngrim in *The Little House On The Prairie*?
5. Which US series of the 1960s featured a servant called Silas?
6. Which actor played a Rovers Return landlord and also played Joe Wilson in *Peak Practice*?
7. What model of Ford car did the police officers drive in *Z Cars*?
8. Which soap featured a pub called Lou's Place?
9. Pencross Fell is a landmark in which British soap?
10. In *Brookside*, in which club were Jason and Greg Shadwick killed?

ANSWERS

1. Blair General, in *Dr Kildare* 2. *The Waltons* 3. *Baywatch* 4. Nellie Oleson 5. *The Big Valley* 6. Roy Barraclough 7. *Zephyr* 8. *Neighbours* 9. *Emmerdale* 10. The Millennium Club

QUIZ 105

1 In which TV pub has the actress Sally Lindsay worked behind the bar?

2 How did the villainous Steve Owen die in *EastEnders*?

3 In *Peyton Place* which character was played by George Macready and Wilfred Hyde-White

4 What was the job of Thomas in *Upstairs Downstairs*?

5 What does the CJ stand for with regard to the *Baywatch* charater CJ Parker?

6 What is the name of Perry Mason's secretary?

7 Who is the longest-ever serving actor in *The Archers*?

8 What was Nick Pascoe's rank in *Soldier Soldier*?

9 What was the nationality of the character played by Andrew Kazamia in *London's Burning*?

10 In *Coronation Street* what was the name of Peter Barlow's twin sister?

ANSWERS

1. The Rovers Return 2. His car exploded after crashing 3. Martin Peyton 4. Chauffeur 5. Casey Jean 6. Della Street 7. Norman Painting 8. Lieutenant 9. Greek 10. Susan

QUIZ 106

Unravel the anagrams to give the names of *Coronation Street* characters.

1. SHES A PLANER
2. SOFT BARREL
3. A YETIS DEED
4. A HIDDEN LOG
5. NETWORK LIE
6. REGENCY SPUD
7. A PLOT BREWER
8. DOT SNOBBERY
9. IRON CLOSER
10. FILLETED ROT

ANSWERS

1. Ena Sharples 2. Alf Roberts 3. Eddie Yeats 4. Hilda Ogden 5. Derek Wilton 6. Percy Sugden 7. Peter Barlow 8. Tyrone Dobbs 9. Norris Cole 10. Fred Elliott

QUIZ 107

1. In which US state is *Picket Fences* set?
2. Who was sacked from his *Neighbours* role of Joe Scully?
3. What is the name of the school in *Home And Away*?
4. Who has played the role of Rita Sullivan in *Coronation Street* for many years?
5. What is the surname of the brothers who played Joe Spencer in *Hollyoaks* and Terry Gibson in *Brookside*?
6. Who plays the role of Mickey Miller in *EastEnders*?
7. In *Neighbours* what was the name of the French exchange student who shared the home of Harold and Madge Bishop?
8. In *EastEnders* which Slater sister announced her engagement to Anthony Trueman?
9. Whom did *Coronation Street* star William Roache impersonate on the TV show *Stars In Their Eyes*?
10. Sheree Murphy of *Emmerdale* fame married which Australian soccer star in real life?

ANSWERS

1. Wisconsin 2. Shane Connor 3. Summer Bay High 4. Barbara Knox 5. Milburn (Matt and Greg) 6. Joe Swash 7. Claire Girard 8. Zoe 9. Perry Como 10. Harry Kewell

QUIZ 108

1. The cast of which medical soap had a 1998 chart hit with the song 'Everlasting Love'?
2. In which century is *Poldark* set?
3. Which two words began each episode of *Dixon Of Dock Green*?
4. What is the name of Hamish Macbeth's West Highland terrier?
5. Which actor has starred in *Duty Free*, *Coronation Street*, *Emmerdale Farm* and *Dr Who*?
6. The Running Stag is the name of a pub in which soap?
7. Who played the husband of Linda Robson in *Birds Of A Feather* and the role of Vic Windsor in *Emmerdale*?
8. Which series was introduced by a theme tune entitled 'Elizabeth Tudor'?
9. In *Coronation Street* what is the name of Kevin Webster's deceased mother?
10. In which city is *Ally McBeal* set?

ANSWERS

1. *Casualty* 2. 18th century 3. "Evening all" 4. Wee Jock 5. Frazer Hines 6. *Crossroads* 7. Alun Lewis 8. *The Forsyte Saga* 9. Alison 10. Boston

QUIZ 109

Unravel the anagrams to give the names of characters from *EastEnders*.

1. A STAGE TWIN
2. BRAVE YARNS
3. WARMER FOLK
4. BARK RUN FETCH
5. A BEAN LIE
6. THIN KNEELERS
7. YIELDED ORE
8. GRIM TENTH CALL
9. WISE JOCK
10. TRICKY CHERUB

ANSWERS

1. Angie Watts 2. Barry Evans 3. Mark Fowler 4. Frank Butcher 5. Ian Beale 6. Ethel Skinner 7. Eddie Royle 8. Grant Mitchell 9. Joe Wicks 10. Ricky Butcher

QUIZ 110

1. The first series of *Upstairs Downstairs* was set in the reign of which king?
2. Erica Davidson was the governor of which soap prison?
3. In which US series is the villain of the piece called Maurice Minnifield?
4. Which series was set in Blake Memorial Hospital?
5. What is the name of Mitch Buchanon's dog in *Baywatch*?
6. In *EastEnders*, who was the stepdaughter of Nigel Bates?
7. What year saw the demise of *Coronation Street* villain Alan Bradley?
8. Who played Leslie Grantham's brother in *The Paradise Club*?
9. Which soap features a police station called City Road?
10. Which butler was played by Robert Guillaume in *Soap*?

ANSWERS

1. Edward VII 2. Wentworth Detention Centre in Prisoner Cell Block H 3. *Northern Exposure* 4. *Marcus Welby MD* 5. Hoby 6. Clare Tyler 7. 1989 8. Don Henderson 9. *Brookside* 10. Benson

QUIZ 111

1. Lou Grant was a spin off from which TV series?
2. What is the name of Grant and Tiffany's daughter in *EastEnders*?
3. Which US soap featured a publication called *Escapade Magazine*?
4. In *Coronation Street* what was the name of Ken Barlow's mother?
5. In which series adapted from a classic novel did Colin Firth play Mr D'Arcy?
6. In *Emmerdale* how did Chris Tate end up in a wheelchair?
7. At which stately home was *Brideshead Revisited* filmed?
8. Which *EastEnders* actor played the son of Al Pacino in the film *Revolution*?
9. Which *Coronation Street* star was born Bernard Popley?
10. What is the name of the local hospital in the US soap *Dallas*?

ANSWERS

1. *The Mary Tyler Moore Show* 2. Courtney 3. *Melrose Place* 4. Ida 5. *Pride And Prejudice* 6. Due to a plane crash 7. Castle Howard 8. Sid Owen 9. Bernard Youens 10. Dallas Memorial Hospital

QUIZ 112

1. Which series was set in the Lancashire town of Hartley?
2. Which former *Coronation Street* star played Vernon Scripps in *Heartbeat*?
3. In which town was the *Z Cars* spin off *Softly Softly* set?
4. What is the first name of Kavanagh QC?
5. Which film provided the inspiration for the series *Dixon Of Dock Green*?
6. Who played PC Fancy Smith in *Z Cars*?
7. Lisa Geoghan plays which character in *The Bill*?
8. What is the first name of Rumpole Of The Bailey?
9. Who played PC Mike Bradley in *Heartbeat*?
10. Who played the title role in *Dixon Of Dock Green*?

ANSWERS

1. *Juliet Bravo* 2. Geoffrey Hughes 3. Wyvern 4. James 5. *The Blue Lamp* 6. Brian Blessed 7. Polly Page 8. Horace 9. Jason Durr 10. Jack Warner

QUIZ 113

• •

1 Which murder suspect was played by the soap star Leslie Grantham in the TV show *Cluedo*?

2 Tadpole, Toadfish and Stonefish are all characters in which soap?

3 In what year did the character of Judy Mallett die in *Coronation Street*?

4 Who links the roles of Tony Vincent in *Casualty* and Tony Horrocks in *Coronation Street*?

5 Which role was played by Tommy Boyle in *Brookside*?

6 Which of the Mitchell clan in *EastEnders* is played by Perry Fenwick?

7 What is the name of Chesney Brown's mother in *Coronation Street*?

8 In which soap did Robbie and Joe set up a fake club called Tanners Against Streakers?

9 Who plays the role of Eileen Grimshaw in *Coronation Street*?

10 Who links the roles of Irene Raymond in *EastEnders* and Gina Gold in *The Bill*?

ANSWERS

1. Colonel Mustard 2. *Neighbours* 3. 1999 4. Lee Warburton 5. Kenny Maguire 6. Billy Mitchell 7. Cilla 8. *Hollyoaks* 9. Sue Cleaver 10. Roberta Taylor

QUIZ 114

1. What is the home state of the Ingalls in *The Little House On The Prairie*?
2. In which year did *The Darling Buds Of May* debut on British TV?
3. What is the name of Jambo's dog in *Hollyoaks*?
4. Blake Carrington in *Dynasty* ran for governor for which state?
5. Who played the role of WPC Young in *The Bill*?
6. In which soap did the character of Dylan Russell accidently kill his mother?
7. Which former *Brookside* star released a cover version of the 1989 hit 'Baby I Don't Care'?
8. Who played Angie Richards in *Emmerdale* before joining the cast of *Coronation Street* in 1989?
9. What was the title of the anti-drugs song that was a hit record for the cast of *Grange Hill*?
10. Which soap featured a corrupt cop called Dougie Slade?

ANSWERS

1. Minnesota 2. 1991 3. Deefer 4. Colorado 5. Beth Cordingly 6. *Home And Away* 7. Jennifer Ellison 8. Beverley Callard 9. 'Just Say No' 10. *EastEnders*

QUIZ 115

Which TV series featured the following public houses?

1 Waterman's Arms
2 The Graffiti Club
3 The Woolpack
4 The Swan
5 The Dog In The Pond
6 The Cattleman's Club
7 The Waterhole
8 Skelthwaite Arms
9 Pomeroy's Wine Bar
10 Aidensfield Arms

ANSWERS

1. *Albion Market* 2. *Coronation Street* 3. *Emmerdale* 4. *Brookside* 5. *Hollyoaks* 6. *Dallas* 7. *Neighbours* 8. *Where The Heart Is* 9. *Rumpole Of The Bailey* 10. *Heartbeat*

QUIZ 116

1. What time of the day provided the nickname of Fusilier Rawlings in *Soldier Soldier*?
2. Which soap features a barmaid called Sadie Hargreaves?
3. In *Brookside* who endured a court trial, accused of murdering Imelda Clough?
4. In *Coronation Street*, who gave Raquel Wolstenhulme French lessons?
5. Which former star of *All Creatures Great And Small* plays the role of Brendan McGuire in the BBC soap *Doctors*?
6. Which star of *Upstairs Downstairs* went on to play the title role in the film *Shirley Valentine*?
7. Which character is played by Tammin Sursock in *Home And Away*?
8. Which star of the soap *Peyton Place* later became the father-in-law of John McEnroe?
9. In *EastEnders*, where did Jim Branning propose to Dot Cotton?
10. In which year did the loveable rogue Eddie Yeats first appear in *Coronation Street*?

ANSWERS

1. Midnight 2. *Hollyoaks* 3. Anthony Murray 4. Ken Barlow 5. Christopher Timothy 6. Pauline Collins 7. Dani Sutherland 8. Ryan O'Neal 9. On the London Eye ride 10. 1974

QUIZ 117

1. Which city is home to the hospital that featured in the docu-soap *Jimmy's*?
2. What is the name of the local newspaper in *Hollyoaks*?
3. What is the name Gary short for with regard to the soap character Gary Ewing?
4. Who does Chris Chittell play in *Emmerdale*?
5. What is the closest major city to *Falcon Crest*?
6. In *Coronation Street*, what kind of shop did Peter Barlow's wife Lucy work in?
7. Which soap featured a priest called Father Gibbons?
8. In *Neighbours*, was the character of Mike Young known for playing the guitar, the saxophone or the piano?
9. Which actor connects the roles of Vinny Sorrell in *Coronation Street* and Governor Grayling in *Bad Girls*?
10. In *Coronation Street*, which couple fostered Sharon Gaskell?

ANSWERS

1. Leeds 2. *The Chester Herald* 3. Garrison 4. Eric Pollard 5. San Francisco 6. Florist's 7. *Brookside* 8. Saxophone 9. James Gaddas 10. Len and Rita Fairclough

QUIZ 118

What are the first names of the following soap characters?

1. Dr Legg in *EastEnders*
2. Pop Larkin in *The Darling Buds Of May*
3. Dr Ross in *ER*
4. Dixon of *Dock Green*
5. DCI Meadows in *The Bill*
6. Lofty Holloway in *EastEnders*
7. Dr Barratt in *Casualty*
8. Reverend Hinton in *Emmerdale*
9. Dr Gibbons in *Neighbours*
10. Dr Kennedy in *Neighbours*

ANSWERS

1. Harold 2. Sidney 3. Douglas 4. George 5. Jack 6. George 7. Mike 8. Donald 9. Clive 10. Karl

QUIZ 119

1. What is the name of Rumpole Of The Bailey's wife?
2. In which area of London was the medical soap *Angels* set?
3. What was Vicky McDonald's maiden name before her *Coronation Street* marriage to Steve McDonald?
4. Which East End character did Dot Cotton help to die in a euthanasia plot?
5. Who plays the role of Steph Scully in *Neighbours*?
6. Who has played a doctor in *Peak Practice*, a bricklayer in *Auf Wiedersehen Pet* and a DS in *Inspector Morse*?
7. In *Brookside*, who had a lesbian relationship with Margaret Clemence?
8. How was Ken Barlow's mother killed?
9. In *Dynasty* what was the name of Blake Carrington's father?
10. Which Weatherfield role was played by Tracy Brabin?

ANSWERS

1. Hilda 2. Battersea 3. Vicky Arden 4. Ethel Skinner 5. Carla Bonner 6. Kevin Whately 7. Beth Jordache 8. Knocked down by a bus 9. Tom 10. Tricia Armstrong

QUIZ 120

1. In *Coronation Street* what was the nickname of Tom Whiteley?
2. In which stage musical did former *Neighbours* star Jason Donovan wear a multi-coloured coat?
3. Which star of *Birds Of A Feather* previously played an ex-convict called Wanda Wise in *Crossroads*?
4. In which state was the 1980s US soap *Santa Barbara* set?
5. Which Dallas character narrated the spin-off show *Dallas: The Early Years*?
6. Which song was a chart-topping collaboration for former *Neighbours* stars Kylie Minogue and Jason Donovan in 1988?
7. In which series did John Stride play the head of the Coleman family?
8. Which soap veteran played the role of Iris McKay in *Beverly Hills 90210*?
9. In which city is *Quincy* set?
10. What was the title of the series in which Nick Berry played a photographer?

ANSWERS

1. Chalkie 2. *Joseph And The Technicolour Dreamcoat* 3. Linda Robson 4. California 5. JR Ewing 6. 'Especially For You' 7. *Diamonds* 8. Stephanie Beacham 9. Los Angeles 10. *Paparazzo*

QUIZ 121

1. Before joining the cast of *EastEnders*, Wendy Richard played Miss Brahms in which sitcom?
2. Who played the title role in *Carry On Cleo* before treading the cobbled streets of *Coronation Street*?
3. Which star of *Dallas* previously played an astronaut called Tony Nelson in *I Dream Of Jeannie*?
4. In which children's TV show did *Coronation Street* star Sue Nicholls play Nadia Popov?
5. Who played Rose Millar in *Tenko* before landing a leading role in *Dynasty*?
6. Who provided backing vocals for the 1980s pop star Mari Wilson before finding fame as the wife of Ian Beale?
7. In which adventure series did *Dallas* good guy Patrick Duffy play Mark Harris?
8. Which former presenter of Blue Peter was cast in the *Emmerdale* role of Adam Forrester?
9. Who starred in the films *Convoy* and *Love Story* before joining the cast of *Dynasty*?
10. In which 1980 film was *Casualty* star Derek Thompson killed by Bob Hoskins?

ANSWERS

1. *Are You Being Served?* 2. Amanda Barrie 3. Larry Hagman 4. *Rentaghost* 5. Stephanie Beacham 6. Michelle Collins 7. *The Man From Atlantis* 8. Tim Vincent 9. Ali MacGraw 10. *The Long Good Friday*

QUIZ 122

1. Which soap was advertised with the publicity slogan 'Sex, Sun and Sangria'?
2. What was Elsie Tanner's favourite drink in the Rovers Return?
3. What surname was shared by Tom, Danny, Maria and Shane in *Neighbours*?
4. What was the nickname of the school bully played by Mark Savage in *Grange Hill*?
5. Which Swedish port did the ferry travel to in the 1980s soap *Triangle*?
6. What is the name Sable short for with regard to the soap character Sable Colby?
7. In which county is *Heartbeat* set?
8. 'Red Alert' was the title of the theme music to which British medical soap?
9. In which year of the 1990s did Robson and Jerome leave the cast of *Soldier Soldier*?
10. In *Casualty*, who played a consultant called Julian Chapman?

ANSWERS

1. *Eldorado* 2. Gin and tonic 3. Ramsay 4. Gripper 5. Gothenburg 6. Sabella 7. Yorkshire 8. *General Hospital* 9. 1995 10. Nigel Le Valliant

QUIZ 123

1. Which former *Coronation Street* star played the role of Dale Sizemore in the Hollywood blockbuster *Black Hawk Down*?
2. Who plays the role of Nana Moon in *EastEnders*?
3. The Boulter family joined which soap in 2003?
4. Which PC played by Scott Neal in *The Bill* was at the centre of a gay storyline?
5. Which former star of *The New Avengers* went on to play Charlie Doyle in *Night And Day*?
6. What connects the jobs of Sinbad in *Brookside* and Stanley Ogden in *Coronation Street*?
7. Who played Constance Mackenzie in the 1957 film version of *Peyton Place*?
8. On which 1980 number one hit did *Coronation Street* star Sally Lindsay sing as a schoolgirl?
9. In *Peak Practice* what is the medical occupation of the character of Kerri Davidson?
10. Which Scottish soap features the character of Dr Andy Sharpe?

ANSWERS

1. Matthew Marsden 2. Hilda Braid 3. *Hollyoaks* 4. PC Luke Ashton 5. Gareth Hunt 6. Both were window cleaners 7. Lana Turner 8. 'There's No One Quite Like Grandma' 9. Physiotherapist 10. *Take The High Road*

QUIZ 124

1. Which star of *Peyton Place* went on to play the female lead in the film *The Great Gatsby*?
2. Who played Auntie Wainwright in *Last Of The Summer Wine* after leaving Weatherfield?
3. Which sitcom, set in a hairdressing salon, starred former *Eastender* Anita Dobson?
4. The TV sitcom *Hardware* stars which former *Coronation Street* actor?
5. Who played PC Litten in *The Bill* before starring as the head of the Porter family in *2.4 Children*?
6. Which former *Brookside* stalwart went on to play the title role in the detective drama *Nice Guy Eddie*?
7. In the TV drama *24* which former *Neighbours* star played the vice president of the USA?
8. Who played Tim Larkins in *Neighbours* and went on to win an Oscar for the film *Gladiator*?
9. Which former star of *Casualty* played the 'pigeon lady' in the film *Home Alone II*?
10. In which series did Ross Kemp play SAS leader Henno Garvie after leaving *EastEnders*?

ANSWERS

1. Mia Farrow 2. Jean Alexander 3. *Split Ends* 4. Ken Morley 5. Gary Olsen 6. Ricky Tomlinson 7. Alan Dale 8. Russell Crowe 9. Brenda Fricker 10. *Ultimate Force*

QUIZ 125

1. Which *Home And Away* villain ran away with Kirsty Sutherland?
2. Which TV soap is set in the town of Charnham?
3. In *Casualty* how did Nurse Sam Colloby die?
4. Who has played Susan in *Heartbeat*, Maggie in *Holby City* and Ros in *Where The Heart Is*?
5. Who played the role of Stephanie Barnes in *Coronation Street*?
6. In which series did Fred Savage play Kevin Arnold?
7. In *The Waltons* what was the name of Olivia Walton?
8. Which character was played by Deborah Shelton in *Dallas*?
9. In which country was the soap actress Pat Phoenix born?
10. Which country did PC Rowan move to when he left Aidensfield in *Heartbeat*?

ANSWERS

1.Kane Phillips 2. *Family Affairs* 3. Pushed off a balcony 4. Samantha Beckinsale 5. Amelia Bullmore 6. *The Wonder Years* 7. Olivia Daly 8. Mandy Winger 9. Ireland 10. Canada

QUIZ 126

1. Which Grimshaw brother is played by Ryan Thomas in *Coronation Street*?
2. Which soap featured a boutique called Jenna's?
3. What is the name of Zoe Tate's daughter in *Emmerdale*?
4. Which former *Hollyoaks* star went on to play Kyle Pascoe in *Footballers' Wives*?
5. Which former *EastEnders* star plays the mother of Kyle Pascoe in *Footballers' Wives*?
6. Which Hollywood star plays the role of Sam Seaborn in *The West Wing*?
7. What is Bobby Ewing's middle name?
8. In which Australian soap did the girl band Atomic Kitten enjoy a cameo role?
9. Which *Coronation Street* character was romantically involved with both the wife and daughter of Ken Barlow?
10. In *London's Burning* what nickname was given to the character of Sally Fields?

ANSWERS

1. Jason 2. *Dallas* 3. Jean 4. Gary Lucy 5. Gillian Taylforth 6. Rob Lowe 7. James 8. *Home And Away* 9. Dev Alahan 10. Gracie

QUIZ 127

1 Who played Batman's arch foe The Joker before landing the role of Peter Stavros in *Falcon Crest*?

2 In which children's soap did Julia Sawalha play the editor of a newspaper?

3 Who won an Oscar for his role in the film *Cool Hand Luke* and went on to join the cast of *Dallas*?

4 Who played a barmaid called Maureen in *Only Fools And Horses* prior to her role of Viv Martella in *The Bill*?

5 Who played the title roles in the TV shows *Private Schulz* and *Boon* before moving to Walford?

6 In which 1969 film did Katherine Ross of *The Colbys*, play the girlfriend of Robert Redford?

7 In which series did the *Street* star Brian Capron play a schoolteacher called Mr Hopwood?

8 Who topped the charts as a teenager in the 1960s and starred in *Albion Market* as an adult in the 1980s?

9 Who played Saucy Nancy in *Worzel Gummidge* before turning up in the Queen Vic?

10 Who portrayed Lord Langdon in *The Colbys* having previously played Lee Crane in *Voyage To The Bottom Of The Sea*?

ANSWERS

1. Cesar Romero 2. *Press Gang* 3. George Kennedy 4. Nula Conwell 5. Michael Elphick 6. *Butch Cassidy And The Sundance Kid* 7. *Grange Hill* 8. Helen Shapiro 9. Barbara Windsor 10. David Hedison

QUIZ 128

1. In *Coronation Street* who read the eulogy at the funeral of the murdered Maxine Peacock?
2. In June 2003 the 400th episode of which medical soap was screened?
3. In which series did former *Soldier Soldier* star Jerome Flynn play DC Tom McCabe?
4. Who wrote the series *Civvies* and *Widows*?
5. The biography *The Queen Of The Street* chronicles the life of which soap star?
6. Which series features a police station called Christmas Street?
7. What is the name Roy short for in the name of Roy Cropper?
8. Who plays the role of Pete Gifford in *Cold Feet*?
9. What was the title of the *EastEnders* special that told of life in Albert Square during World War II?
10. During which queen's reign was the medical drama *Bramwell* set?

ANSWERS

1. Her killer, Richard Hillman 2. *Casualty* 3. *Badger* 4. Lynda La Plante 5. Julie Goodyear 6. *City Central* 7. Royston 8. John Thomson 9. *Civvy Street* 10. Queen Victoria

QUIZ 129

1. Which series featured a sailing vessel called the *Flying Fish*?
2. Which girlfriend of Curly Watts was played by Suzanne Hall?
3. In *Brookside*, which member of the Corkhill family was played by Justine Kerrigan?
4. Who plays the role of Nita Desai in *Coronation Street*?
5. What was the title of the *Coronation Street* spin-off in which Steve McDonald travels to Calais?
6. What was the name of the *Crossroads* Motel's Scottish chef?
7. In which decade is *The Darling Buds Of May* set?
8. What was the title of the *Emmerdale* spin-off that featured the Dingle family on vacation in Australia?
9. What was the nationality of the *EastEnders* character Ali Osman?
10. Which former *Street* star went on to play Lauren Harris in *Fat Friends*?

ANSWERS

1. *Howard's Way* 2. Kimberley Taylor 3. Tracy 4. Rebecca Sarker 5. *After Hours* 6. Shughie McFee 7. 1950s 8. *The Dingles Down Under* 9. Turkish 10. Gaynor Faye

QUIZ 130

1 In which comedy series did Jean Alexander play the mother of Patricia Hodge?

2 Who played the daughter in *McCready And Daughter* after leaving Albert Square?

3 Who plays Dr Sam Ryan in *Silent Witness* having previously appeared in *Brookside*?

4 In which series did former *Soldier Soldier* star Robson Green play the Geordie brother of Stephen Tompkinson?

5 Which *ER* star went on to play Batman on film?

6 Who played Dr Vincent Markham in *Peyton Place* before becoming a Hollywood comedy actor?

7 Who appeared naked in the stage play *The Blue Room* after leaving *Coronation Street*?

8 Which *Casualty* star went on to provide a love interest for Geraldine Grainger in *The Vicar Of Dibley*?

9 Who left *EastEnders* in 1997 and went on to play the title role in the 2001 film *Goodbye Charlie Bright*?

10 Which *Coronation Street* star chronicled the true story of Coral Atkins in the TV drama *Seeing Red*?

ANSWERS

1. *Rich Tea And Sympathy* 2. Patsy Palmer 3. Amanda Burton 4. *Grafters* 5. George Clooney 6. Leslie Nielsen 7. Tracy Shaw 8. Clive Mantle 9. Paul Nicholls 10. Sarah Lancashire

QUIZ 131

1. Which *Brookside* character has been played by Debbie Reynolds and Diane Burke?
2. In which series did Amanda Redman play a housewife who won £38 million on the lottery?
3. Which soap had the original working title of *East 8*?
4. What was Harry Clayton's job in Weatherfield?
5. What is the home county of the Gilder family in *Born And Bred*?
6. In which prostitute drama did Barbara Dickson play the role of Amanda?
7. Who plays the role of TJ Middleditch in *The Royal*?
8. Who played the role of Barbara Brady in *Crossroads*?
9. In which city is the series *Clocking Off* set?
10. Which series co-stars Pauline Quirke and Warren Clarke as a married couple called Faith and Brian Addis?

ANSWERS

1. Katy Rogers 2. *At Home With The Braithwaites* 3. *EastEnders* 4. Milkman 5. Lancashire 6. *Band Of Gold* 7. Ian Carmichael 8. Sue Lloyd 9. Manchester 10. *Down To Earth*

QUIZ 132

1. Which star of *EastEnders* had a novelty hit record with the song 'The Ugly Duckling'?
2. What is the nickname of the *Home And Away* character Ruth Stewart?
3. Who does Jay Bunyan play in *Neighbours*?
4. Which former Eastender played Eddie Scrooge in an updated version of *A Christmas Carol* in 2000?
5. Which movie star played the role of Tony Cumson in *Falcon Crest*?
6. At the start of 2004 who was the longest-serving male character in *EastEnders*?
7. At the start of 2004 who was the longest-serving female character in *EastEnders*?
8. In which 1980s series did Brigit Forsyth play Dr Judith Vincent?
9. In which US soap did Michael Ironside play a doctor nicknamed Wild Willy?
10. Against which sport was the soap mini-series *Riders* set?

ANSWERS

1. Mike Reid 2. Roo 3. Jack Scully 4. Ross Kemp 5. John Saxon 6. Ian Beale 7. Pauline Fowler 8. *The Practice* 9. *ER* 10. Showjumping

QUIZ 133

In *Coronation Street* ...

1 Who was revealed as Ashley Peacock's father?
2 Who plays Deidre Rachid's mother?
3 How many sons has Jim McDonald fathered?
4 Who are the parents of Sophie and Rosie?
5 What is the name of Nick Tilsley's deceased father?
6 Who was the father of Fiona Middleton's son, Morgan?
7 Born in 1995, who is Daniel Osbourne's father?
8 What is the name of Tyrone Dobbs's mother?
9 What is the name of Vikram Desai's father?
10 In 1999 which couple celebrated the birth of Christmas Day twins?

ANSWERS

1. Fred Elliott 2. Maggie Jones 3. Two 4. Sally and Kevin Webster 5. Brian 6. Alan McKenna .7. Ken Barlow 8. Jackie 9. Ravi 10. Gary and Judy Mallett

QUIZ 134

1. Which series revolves around Castlefield Blues ladies' football team?
2. In which soap does the Ardnacraig Hotel feature?
3. Which series sees former *EastEnders* star Michelle Collins playing a divorced mother of two called Sarah Barton?
4. Which soap actor sang 'Wind Beneath My Wings' when he was a subject on *This Is Your Life*?
5. What is the name Cat short for with regard to *Family Affairs* character Cat Webb?
6. Which series has featured nurses called Sally Boothe, Peggy Snow and Ruth Goddard?
7. Who has played Dawn in *Brookside*, Hannah in *Casualty* and Sharon in *EastEnders*?
8. Which Weatherfield character is played by Kathryn Hunt?
9. What was the first name of the character played by Robson Green in *Soldier Soldier*?
10. Which series was set on an oil rig called the *Osprey Explorer*?

ANSWERS

1. *Playing The Field* 2. *High Road* 3. *Single* 4. Bill Tarmey 5. Catriona 6. *Where The Heart Is* 7. Leticia Dean 8. Angela Harris 9. Dave 10. *Roughnecks*

QUIZ 135

1 In which year did the medical soap *Angels* make its screen farewell?

2 In which US soap did a business called Valentine's Lingerie feature?

3 Which member of The Beatles did *EastEnders* star John Altman play on film?

4 In which series did Gwyneth Strong, Pauline Quirke and Michelle Collins play school friends reunited for a hen night?

5 What was the title of the series that saw Robson Green and Francesca Annis embroiled in an illicit love affair?

6 In *The Colbys* what political post was held by Cash Cassidy?

7 Who links the roles of Dawn in *Frank Stubbs Promotes* and Sam in *EastEnders*?

8 What was Valerie Barlow's maiden name in *Coronation Street*?

9 Who played Bond girl Holly Goodhead in *Moonraker* and also played Holly Harwood in *Dallas*?

10 Which actress, better known for her comedy roles, played the role of Madge Green in *EastEnders*?

ANSWERS

1. 1983 2. *Dallas* 3. George Harrison 4. *Real Women* 5. *Reckless* 6. Senator 7. Danniella Westbrook 8. Tatlock 9. Lois Chiles 10. Pat Coombs

QUIZ 136

1. Which *Hollyoaks* character is nicknamed OB?
2. Which character attempted to burn down her school after a row concerning an art project?
3. In the show, what kind of shop is Got It Taped?
4. Which character married Ruth Osborne?
5. What was the nickname of James Bolton played in the show by Will Mellor?
6. Which *Hollyoaks* character committed suicide in October 2001?
7. Which *Hollyoaks* character is usually referred to as Finn?
8. Who plays the role of Ben Davies in the show?
9. Who played the role of Luke in *Hollyoaks* and went on to play Kyle in *Footballers' Wives*?
10. The *Hollyoaks* character Brian Morgan is an avid fan of which fictional Scottish football team?

ANSWERS

1. Sam O'Brien 2. Zara Morgan 3. Video shop 4. Kurt Benson 5. Jambo 6. Lewis Richardson 7. Rory Finnegan 8. Marcus Patric 9. Gary Lucy 10. Cowdenbeath

QUIZ 137

• •

1. Who played the role of Steve Hackett in the crime series *Target* before joining the cast of *Emmerdale*?
2. In *Coronation Street* who had an affair with her Australian cousin Ian Latimer?
3. Who links the roles of Tommy Mullaney in *LA Law* and Leo McGarry in *The West Wing*?
4. Which soap character married Clayton Farlow?
5. In 2001 who became the official PA and live-in lover of Chris Tate in *Emmerdale*?
6. Which series featured the character of Reverend Alden?
7. Which character in *Neighbours* was nicknamed Button?
8. Which series features a holiday company called Janus Holidays?
9. In which series did Peter Barkworth play a banking executive called Mark Telford?
10. What show ended with Angus Hudson tying the knot with Kate Bridges?

ANSWERS

1. Patrick Mower 2. Gail Tilsley 3. John Spencer 4. Miss Ellie Ewing 5. Charity Dingle 6. *The Little House On The Prairie* 7. Hannah Martin 8. *Sunburn* 9. *Telford's Change* 10. *Upstairs Downstairs*

QUIZ 138

• •

1. Which star of *EastEnders* penned an autobiography entitled *Kathy And Me*?
2. In which soap did the broadcaster Clive James enjoy a cameo role as a postman?
3. Who made her *Carry On* debut in *Carry On Spying* and, later, her *EastEnders* debut in 1994?
4. Which soap opera star published an autobiography entitled *Vamp Until Ready*?
5. Which role is played by Luke Tittensor in *Emmerdale*?
6. Who played the roles of Mrs Duffin in *Casualty* and Mrs Warboys in *One Foot In The Grave*?
7. Which series featured a pub called the Oliver Twist?
8. Who narrated *The Waltons*?
9. Which Australian soap featured a wombat called Fatso?
10. Who is the third person to play Janine, the daughter of Frank Butcher in *EastEnders*?

ANSWERS

1. Gillian Taylforth 2. *Neighbours* 3. Barbara Windsor 4. Kate O'Mara 5. Daz Hopwood 6. Doreen Mantle 7. *London's Burning* 8. Earl Hamner 9. *A Country Practice* 10. Charlie Brooks

QUIZ 139

1. In *Dallas* what is the name of the father of Cliff Barnes?
2. What is the name of JR and Bobby Ewings brother who moved to California?
3. What is the name of the Ewings ranch?
4. Who played Pam Ewing?
5. Which former wife of a famous pop star played Jenna Wade?
6. In *Dynasty* which British actor played Ben Carrington?
7. Which *Dynasty* star was the second wife of the film director John Derek?
8. Which congressman was played in the show by Paul Burke?
9. What was the name of the oil company that Alexis inherited following the death of her husband Cecil Colby?
10. How is Alexis related to Sable Colby?

ANSWERS

1. Digger Barnes 2. Gary 3. Southfork 4. Victoria Principal 5. Priscilla Presley 6. Christopher Cazenove 7. Linda Evans 8. Neal McVane 9. Colbyco 10. Cousins

QUIZ 140

1 What is the nickname of Ronnie Silver in *London's Burning*?

2 What was the name of the religious cult that committed mass suicide at 5, Brookside Close?

3 Was Larry Hagman born in 1931, 1932 or 1933?

4 Which *Coronation Street* character owned a boutique called The Western Front?

5 In *Neighbours* what was the name of Helen Daniels' adopted daughter?

6 Which 1980s soap mini-series starred Jane Seymour as Cathy Ames?

7 Who joined the cast of *Emmerdale* in 2004 in the role of Val Lambert?

8 In *Neighbours* which fictional football club did Jack Scully play for in England?

9 Which Weatherfield landlady was played by Vivienne Ross?

10 *A Woman To Remember* was the title of the first-ever TV soap in which country?

ANSWERS

1. Hi Ho 2. The Church Of Simon 3. 1931 4. Mike Baldwin 5. Rosemary 6. *East Of Eden* 7. Charlie Hardwick 8. Barnsford FC 9. Stella Rigby 10. USA

QUIZ 141

1 Who plays the role of Gus Smith in *EastEnders*?

2 On November 22, 1980 an estimated 27 million UK viewers tuned in to which soap opera?

3 What connects Natalie Price in *EastEnders* and Annie Walker in *Coronation Street*?

4 In which year will *Coronation Street* celebrate its Golden Anniversary and *EastEnders* its Silver Anniversary?

5 Which Ramsay Street maneater is played by Natalie Bassingthwaighte?

6 Which employee of Weatherfield council was played by Roberta Kerr and had an affair with Ken Barlow?

7 Which comedy actor played the role of Sid Hooper in *Crossroads*?

8 Which TV game show has been presented by *EastEnders* star Leslie Grantham and Christopher Ellison of *The Bill*?

9 Which soap featured the characters of Razor Sharpe and Dieter Shultz?

10 Which Weatherfield temptress was portrayed by Cheryl Murray?

ANSWERS

1. Mohammed George 2. Dallas (the episode that revealed who shot JR) 3. Both played by Speeds (Lucy and Doris) 4. 2010 5. Izzy Holland 6. Wendy Crosier 7. Stan Stennett 8. Fort Boyard 9. *Eldorado* 10. Suzie Birchall

QUIZ 142

1. Who moved into No 3 Coronation Street in 1988 as Emily Bishop's lodger?
2. Who left No 7 Coronation Street to become a beauty consultant?
3. What type of birds did Jack Duckworth keep in the backyard of No 9 Coronation Street?
4. Which married couple moved into No 4 Coronation Street in 1990?
5. Which resident of No 1 Coronation Street became Mrs Robert Preston in 1996?
6. Which family bought No 11 Coronation Street from Alf Roberts?
7. What number of Coronation Street is The Kabin?
8. Who lived at No 13 Coronation Street for 23 years?
9. Which resident of No 5 Coronation Street was charged with the attempted murder of Alma Baldwin in 1996?
10. Who sold the Coronation Street hairdressing salon to Fiona Middleton?

ANSWERS

1. Percy Sugden 2. Raquel Watts 3. Pigeons 4. Mavis and Derek Wilton 5. Tracy Barlow 6. The McDonalds 7. No 10 8. Hilda Ogden 9. Don Brennan 10. Denise Osbourne

QUIZ 143

1. The river Hamble provided the setting for which soap?
2. In which year of the 21st century did Dennis Stringer die in *Coronation Street*?
3. Which former model played the role of Lady Janet Whitly in *Heartbeat*?
4. In which country is the soap opera *All Saints* set?
5. Who plays PC Carver in *The Bill*?
6. Which actor replaced Martin Sheen as president of the USA in *The West Wing*?
7. Which soap featured a store called Firmans Freezers?
8. In which year did Kylie Minogue top the charts with 'I Should Be So Lucky'?
9. Was Jock Ewing's first wife called Amy, Anne or Amanda?
10. In which country was Bet Lynch's son killed?

ANSWERS

1. *Howard's Way* 2. 2002 3. Twiggy 4. Australia 5. Mark Wingett 6. John Goodman 7. *Coronation Street* 8. 1988 9. Amanda 10. Northern Ireland

QUIZ 144

1. Which serial killer's funeral was held in *Hollyoaks* in January 2004?
2. With which teenager did Martin Platt begin a Weatherfield affair in 2003?
3. Who played the role of Roy Evans in *EastEnders*?
4. Which former singing star plays Sergeant Sheelagh Murphy in *The Bill*?
5. Who plays the Rovers Return potman Harry Flagg?
6. In *Family Affairs* is Doug McKenzie a builder, a postman or a policeman?
7. Who links the roles of Dr Marc Elliot in *Doctors* and PC Steve Loxton in *The Bill*?
8. Which soap featured a crime boss called Rocco Cammeniti?
9. In *EastEnders* who beat up Graham Foster in a revenge attack for raping Little Mo?
10. Which member of the Platt family is played by Jack Peter Shepherd in *Coronation Street*?

ANSWERS

1. Toby Mills 2. Katy Harris 3. Tony Caunter 4. Bernie Nolan 5. Iain Rogerson 6. A builder 7. Tom Butcher 8. *Neighbours* 9. Charlie Slater 10. David Platt

QUIZ 145

1. In which year was *London's Burning* first screened on British TV?
2. What nickname was given to Roland Cartwright's character?
3. Who wrote the play on which the series was based?
4. Who played the firefighter Kevin Medhurst in the series?
5. What nickname was given to Mike Wilson's character?
6. Which star of *London's Burning* was jailed in 1999 for drug offences?
7. What was Lisa Hill's job at the fire station?
8. Which daughter of Richard Beckinsale played the role of Kate Stevens?
9. In which year did the series end?
10. What nickname was given to the hypochondriac character of Bert Quigley?

ANSWERS

1. 1988 2. Vaseline 3. Jack Rosenthal 4. Ross Boatman 5. Bayleaf 6. John Alford 7. Cook 8. Samantha Beckinsale 9. 2002 10. Sicknote

QUIZ 146

1 Which former star of *The Liver Birds* plays Diane Blackstock in *Emmerdale*?

2 In which series did Helen Baxendale play Dr Claire Maitland?

3 Which crooked cop murdered DS Boulton in *The Bill*?

4 In which war did Holly and June Forsyte serve as nurses?

5 In which soap did Nikki Marshall leave Jim Brodie standing at the altar?

6 In which soap did Kate Patrick embark on an incestuous affair with her twin brother Joe?

7 Which soap features a landmark called Tommy Deakin's Arch?

8 Was *Dynasty* star Joan Collins born in 1931, 1932 or 1933?

9 In which soap did the character of George Manners spread a virus that he contracted in Kenya?

10 Which *Summer Bay* curmudgeon is played by Ray Meagher?

ANSWERS

1. Elizabeth Estensen 2. *Cardiac Arrest* 3. Don Beech 4. The Boer War 5. *Holby City* 6. *Hollyoaks* 7. *Coronation Street* 8. 1933 9. *Brookside* 10. Alf Stewart

QUIZ 147

1. Who set fire to the Dagmar wine bar in *EastEnders*?
2. Which series features a student nurse called Samantha Beaumont?
3. In *EastEnders*, what is the name of Barry Evans' scheming younger brother?
4. The *Coronation Street* character Tommy Harris is an avid fan of which Yorkshire football club?
5. In *The Bill*, what nationality is PC Cameron Tait?
6. What nationality were the characters of Lam Quoc Hoa and Ly Nhu Chan in *Albion Market*?
7. In *Neighbours* what did Cheryl Stark name her pub?
8. In which Australian soap did Simon Bowen walk down the aisle with Vicky Dean?
9. Which US soap is set in the town of Pine Valley?
10. In *Dallas*, who is Lucy Ewing's father?

ANSWERS

1. Dennis Watts 2. *The Royal* 3. Nathan 4. Sheffield Wednesday 5. Australian 6. Vietnamese 7. Chez Chez 8. *A Country Practice* 9. *All My Children* 10. Gary Ewing

QUIZ 148

Name the actors who have played the following soap characters.

1. Norris Cole in *Coronation Street*
2. Zara Morgan in *Hollyoaks*
3. Don Lockwood in *Dallas*
4. DC Dashwood in *The Bill*
5. Izzy Davies in *Hollyoaks*
6. Angel Samson in *Crossroads*
7. Arnold Becker in *LA Law*
8. Ray Hilton in *Brookside*
9. Ellie Mills in *Hollyoaks*
10. Tina Seabrook in *Casualty*

ANSWERS

1. Malcolm Hebden 2. Kelly Greenwood 3. Ian McShane 4. John Iles 5. Elize du Toit 6. Jane Asher 7. Corbin Bernsen 8. Kenneth Cope 9. Sarah Baxendale 10. Claire Goose

QUIZ 149

1. Arthur White joined the cast of *Hollyoaks* in 2004. Who is his famous real life brother?
2. In which US soap was the town of Truro watched over by Sheriff Titus Semple?
3. Which soap features a restaurant called the Bayside Diner?
4. In *Coronation Street* was Harry Hewitt a milkman, a bus inspector or a fireman?
5. In *Cardia Arrest* was Cyril Smedley nicknamed Stitches, Scalpel or Scissors?
6. Which actor was killed off in *Coronation Street* and went on to play David Buckley in *Where The Heart Is*?
7. Which US soap, first broadcast in 1952, tells the story of the Bauer family?
8. Which video spin-off from *Coronation Street* saw the Duckworths on holiday in Nevada?
9. Which star of *The Bill* also played Harry Blackburn in the second series of *Auf Wiedersehen Pet*?
10. Which character portrayed by Scott Windsor arrived in *Emmerdale* in 2004?

ANSWERS

1. David Jason 2. *Flamingo Road* 3. *Home And Away* 4. Bus inspector 5. Scissors 6. Phil Middlemiss 7. *Guiding Light* 8. *Coronation Street: Viva Las Vegas* 9. Kevin Lloyd 10. Carl King

QUIZ 150

1 Which TV soap was originally entitled *One Way Street*?

2 Who plays David Braithwaite in *At Home With The Braithwaites*?

3 Which PC in *The Bill* served in Northern Ireland for five years in the Queen's Royal Fusiliers Regiment?

4 Who played the title role in *The Flying Nun* and went on to become an Oscar-winning actress?

5 In which series does former *EastEnders* star Linda Coulson play DC Rosie McManus?

6 Which docu-soap introduced viewers to a Norwegian vet called Trude Mostue?

7 Which member of the Dingle clan is played by Andy Devine?

8 In *Coronation Street*, Tyrone Dobbs proposed to Maria Sutherland at the top of which building?

9 Which *Brookside* character underwent a mastectomy operation in 1992?

10 What was the first name of the character played by Jerome Flynn in *Soldier Soldier*?

ANSWERS

1. *Neighbours* 2. Peter Davison 3. Dale Smith or Smithy 4. Sally Field 5. *MIT* 6. *Vets In Practice* 7. Shadrach Dingle 8. Blackpool Tower 9. Patricia Farnham 10. Paddy

QUIZ 151

Name the actors who have played the following soap characters.

1 Jimmy Corkhill in *Brookside*

2 Ted Roach in *The Bill*

3 Monica Colby in *The Colbys*

4 Siobhan Marsden in *Emmerdale*

5 Nellie Harvey in *Coronation Street*

6 Jack Ewing in *Dallas*

7 Ashley Peacock in *Coronation Street*

8 Hattie Tavernier in *EastEnders*

9 Jeff Colby in *Dynasty*

10 Joe Thorn in *Family Affairs*

ANSWERS

1. Dean Sullivan 2. Tony Scannell 3. Tracy Scoggins 4. Abigail Fisher 5. Mollie Sugden 6. Dack Rambo 7. Steven Arnold 8. Michelle Gayle 9. John James 10. Les Dennis

QUIZ 152

1. Which character in *Home And Away* has been played by Joel McIlroy and Martin Dingle Wall?
2. Which US soap featured the Ortega family and the Ranson family?
3. What was Kylie Minogue's first No 1 hit after leaving *Neighbours*?
4. In *Coronation Street*, who played an amorous senior citizen called Wally Bannister in 2003?
5. Which character was pregnant in the very first episode of *EastEnders*?
6. In which series did Pauline Collins and John Alderton play Harriet and Jack Boult?
7. In which city is Perry Mason set?
8. Which *EastEnders* star guested in the role of Captain Tau in the sci-fi sitcom *Red Dwarf*?
9. In which series did Major Voce marry Captain Butler?
10. Which charater returned to *Coronation Street* in 2002 after a seven year absence?

ANSWERS

1. Flynn Saunders 2. *Falcon Crest* 3. 'I Should Be So Lucky' 4. Bernard Cribbins 5. Pauline Fowler 6. *Forever Green* 7. Los Angeles 8. Anita Dobson 9. *Soldier Soldier* 10. Bet Gilroy nee Lynch

QUIZ 153

1. Which character in *Coronation Street* was played by Meg Johnson?
2. What connects Monica and Miles in *Dynasty* with Steve and Andy in *Coronation Street*?
3. In *The Bill* which DCI is played by Simon Rouse?
4. Which member of the Bishop family was played by Kevin Harrington in *Neighbours*?
5. What did Ena Sharples usually wear on her head?
6. In which prison was *The Governor* set?
7. Which *Emmerdale* role did Shirley Stelfox play?
8. Which ex mother-in-law of Reg Holdsworth worked as an assistant in the *Coronation Street* corner shop?
9. Which *EastEnders* star appeared in a TV advert for British Telecom digging his allotment?
10. Who connects the roles of Billy Corkhill in *Brookside* and Terry Tinniswood in *Heartbeat*?

ANSWERS

1. Eunice Gee 2. They are both twin siblings 3. DCI Meadows 4. David Bishop 5. A hairnet 6. Barfield Prison 7. Edna Birch 8. Maud Grimes 9. Bill Treacher 10. John McArdle

QUIZ 154

Name the actors who have played the following soap characters.

1 PC Nick Klein in *The Bill*
2 Trevor Jordache in *Brookside*
3 Linda Baldwin in *Coronation Street*
4 Stephanie Rogers in *Dallas*
5 Megan Roach in *Casualty*
6 Jill Chance in *Crossroads*
7 Zack Dingle in *Emmerdale*
8 Greg Reardon in *Falcon Crest*
9 Billy Walker in *Coronation Street*
10 Sir Edward Frere in *Howard's Way*

ANSWERS

1. Rene Zagger 2. Brian Murray 3. Jacqueline Pirie 4. Lesley Anne Down 5. Brenda Fricker 6. Jane Rossington 7. Steve Halliwell 8. Simon MacCorkindale 9. Ken Farrington 10. Nigel Davenport

QUIZ 155

1. In which soap does Bessie Street School feature?
2. What is the first name of the *Neighbours* character who had the surnames of Mitchell, Ramsay and Bishop?
3. Which member of the Corkhill clan opened a shop called Kowboy Kutz in *Brookside* Parade?
4. Which number one hit did *EastEnders* star Martin Kemp feature on with the band Spandau Ballet?
5. Was Leslie Grantham born in 1946, 1947 or 1948?
6. Which star of *Where The Heart Is* married the football star Lee Chapman?
7. Which *Coronation Street* character has had the surnames of Potter ,Tilsley, Platt and Hillman?
8. Who plays the role of Victoria Merrick in *Holby City*?
9. In which city are *Holby City* and *Casualty* filmed?
10. In *Family Affairs*, what is the family surname of Justin, Yasmin, Doug and Marc?

ANSWERS

1. *Coronation Street* 2. Madge 3. Jimmy Corkhill 4. 'True' 5. 1947 6. Leslie Ash 7. Gail 8. Lisa Faulkner 9. Bristol 10. Mackenzie

QUIZ 156

1 Which of the Kray twins was played by Martin Kemp on film?

2 Which US soap has had episodes entitled *Brandon Leaves* and *Aunt Bea's Pickles*?

3 What surname is shared by Curly in Weatherfield and Angie in Walford?

4 At the 2000 British Soap Awards, which actor received the Lifetime Achievement Award?

5 In *ER* what is the three-letter nickname of Dr David Cvetic?

6 Which soap spanned the most episodes, *Dallas* or *Dynasty*?

7 At which bride's wedding did Emily Nugent meet her future husband Ernest Bishop?

8 Which member of the royal family appeared in a live episode to celebrate the 40th anniversay of *Coronation Street*?

9 What first name is shared by Branning in *EastEnders* and McDonald in *Coronation Street*?

10 Whose ghost returned to *Emmerdale* to console her grieving husband Marlon?

ANSWERS

1. Reggie Kray 2. *Beverly Hills 90210* 3. Watts 4. William Roache 5. Div 6. *Dallas* 7. Elsie Tanner's 8. Prince Charles 9. Jim 10. Tricia Dingle

QUIZ 157

Name the actors who have played the following soap characters.

1 Jack Vincent in *Casualty*
2 Hayley Cropper in *Coronation Street*
3 Beth Jordache in *Brookside*
4 Katherine Wentworth in *Dallas*
5 Virginia Raven in *Crossroads*
6 Jamie Hart in *Family Affairs*
7 Sue Keel in *Peak Practice*
8 Angelica Nero in *Dallas*
9 Vikram Desai in *Coronation Street*
10 Kate Tyler in *EastEnders*

ANSWERS

1. Will Mellor 2. Julie Hesmondhalgh 3. Anna Friel 4. Morgan Brittany 5. Sherrie Hewson 6. Michael Cole 7. Minnie Driver 8. Barbara Carrera 9. Chris Bisson 10. Jill Halfpenny

QUIZ 158

1. In *Neighbours,* who proposed to Lou Carpenter in 2004?
2. Who played the role of Mary Ashe in *Dr Who* before joining the cast of *Coronation Street* in 1974?
3. What is the name of Chris Tate's half-brother who kidnapped him in 1999?
4. Whose son in *Dallas* was played by Tyler Banks and Omri Katz?
5. In what year was the Weatherfield baby Nick Tilsley born?
6. Which docu-soap made a celebrity out of a learner driver called Maureen Rees?
7. How are Cliff Barnes and Pamela Ewing related?
8. What is the name of Ken Barlow's brother?
9. What was the Crossroads Motel renamed as, after it burnt down in 1981?
10. In 2004, which Weatherfield character stole an engagement ring from a jewellers shop?

ANSWERS

1. Trixie Tucker 2. Helen Worth 3. Liam 4. JR Ewing's son 5. 1980 6. *Driving School* 7. Brother and sister 8. David 9. Crossroads, Kings Oak 10. Kirk Sutherland

QUIZ 159

1 In *EastEnders*, where did Grant and Tiffany tie the knot?

2 Which US soap is set in the town of Queens Point?

3 Who narrated the docu-soap *Lad's Army*?

4 In *Neighbours*, what is the name of Brett Starks' twin sister?

5 Which member of *Dynasty*'s Carrington clan was played by Pamela Bellwood?

6 Which soap company signed a sponsorship deal to promote the TV soap *Crossroads*?

7 In *Emmerdale* who is the father of Zoe Tate's baby?

8 Who played the role of Dangerous Davies in *The Last Detective*?

9 In which city is *Sex And The City* set?

10 In which appropriate state was *Dallas* star Larry Hagman born?

ANSWERS

1. Gibraltar 2. *The Young Marrieds* 3. Kevin Whately 4. Danni 5. Claudia Carrington 6. Surf 7. Scott Windsor 8. Peter Davison 9. New York 10. Texas

QUIZ 160

Name the actors who have played the following soap characters.

1. Jim McDonald in *Coronation Street*
2. Sam Curtis in *Flamingo Road*
3. Amy Howard in *Casualty*
4. Debbie Dean in *Hollyoaks*
5. June Ackland in *The Bill*
6. Francis Barratt in *Peak Practice*
7. Meredith Braxton in *Falcon Crest*
8. Dusty Farlow in *Dallas*
9. Samantha Cockerill in *Family Affairs*
10. Judy Mallett in *Coronation Street*

ANSWERS

1. Charles Lawson 2. John Beck 3. Rebecca Wheatley 4. Jodi Albert 5. Trudie Goodwin 6. Sean Pertwee 7. Jane Badler 8. Jared Martin 9. Tessa Wyatt 10. Gaynor Faye

QUIZ 161

1. Who portrayed the lawyer Ling Woo in *Ally McBeal*?
2. Ted Pilkington was a landlord of which Manchester soap pub?
3. In *EastEnders*, which member of the Beale clan died at Christmas 1993?
4. Who played the role of Shannon Reed in *Home And Away*?
5. What is the name of Taj Coppin's brother in *Neighbours*?
6. Which disease claimed the life of *Coronation Street*'s Alma Baldwin?
7. Which Australian soap centred around the activities of Riverside Police Station?
8. Which brewery supplies the beer at the Woolpack in *Emmerdale*?
9. Which star of the musical *Oliver*, joined the cast of *EastEnders* in 2003 as Edwin Caldicot?
10. In *Bad Girls*, which lesbian inmate is played by Alicia Eyo?

ANSWERS

1. Lucy Lui 2. The Waterman's Arms in Albion Market 3. Pete Beale 4. Isla Fisher 5. Tahnee 6. Cancer 7. *Copshop* 8. Ephraim Monk 9. Ron Moody 10. Denny Blood

QUIZ 162

1. What was the title of the TV sequel to *A Bouquet Of Barbed Wire*?
2. Which soap was screened on the opening night schedule of Channel 4?
3. Which star of the comedy series *The Cuckoo Waltz*, plays the role of Julia Parsons in *Doctors*?
4. In which decade was Noele Gordon born?
5. Which Australian soap chronicled the lives of the staff of Pacific International Airport?
6. In *EastEnders* what is the name of Pauline Fowler's youngest son?
7. Which character was played in *Coronation Street* by Veronica Doran?
8. What nationality is Mr Papadopoulos, the owner of the Albert Square launderette?
9. What is the name of Jason Colby's father?
10. Which Weatherfield mechanic employs Tyrone Dobbs?

ANSWERS

1. *Another Bouquet* 2. *Brookside* 3. Diane Keen 4. 1920s 5. *Skyways* 6. Martin 7. Marion Yeats 8. Greek 9. Andrew 10. Kevin Webster

QUIZ 163

1. Under which name did several cast members of *Emmerdale* record the hit song 'Hillbilly Rock'?
2. What is the name of the rival pub to the Woolpack?
3. Who created *Emmerdale* Farm?
4. Which *Emmerdale* role is played by John Middleton?
5. Who moved to Spain with Amos Brearley following their 1995 wedding?
6. Which family moved into Home Farm in 1989?
7. Which actress played a Dingle in *Emmerdale* and an Ogden in *Coronation Street*?
8. Which presenter of the children's show *Magpie* played the role of Briddy Middleton in *Emmerdale*?
9. In *Emmerdale,* which job was held in Beckindale by Donald Hilton from 1977 to 1989?
10. In *Emmerdale,* what is the name of the real life West Yorkshire village where the soap is filmed?

ANSWERS

1. The Woolpackers 2. The Malt Shovel 3. Kevin Laffan 4. Reverend Ashley Thomas 5. Annie Sugden 6. The Tates 7. Sandra Gough 8. Jenny Hanley 9. Village vicar 10. Esholt

QUIZ 164

1. In *Coronation Street,* what was the name of Len Fairclough's son?
2. Which actor had a hit record with the theme song from *Dr Kildare*?
3. What surname links the characters of Darren, Ruth and Natalie in *Hollyoaks*?
4. In which series did Janet McTeer play prison boss Helen Hewitt?
5. Which star of *The Colbys* was born Ruby Stevens?
6. On whose novel was the mini series *Roots* based?
7. PC Gary Best in *The Bill* is an avid fan of which football club?
8. Who composed the theme for *EastEnders*?
9. In the 21st-century version of *The Forsyte Saga* who played the role of Aunt Juley?
10. Which role is played by Danny Raco in *Home And Away*?

ANSWERS

1. Stanley 2. Richard Chamberlain 3. Osborne 4. *The Governor* 5. Barbara Stanwyck 6. Alex Haley 7. Manchester City 8. Simon May 9. Wendy Craig 10. Alex Poulos

QUIZ 165

1. In *Dynasty* what surname is shared by the characters of Claudia, Matthew and Lindsay?
2. On whose novel was the 1980s series, *Hotel* based?
3. When Don Brennan set fire to Mike Baldwin's factory, who did he attempt to frame for the crime?
4. In which soap was a dead woman's body discovered in the Pascoe's swimming pool?
5. In which film did *The Bill* star Mark Wingett appear alongside Sting and Toyah Wilcox?
6. What is the name of Shelley Unwin's mother in *Coronation Street*?
7. Who links the roles of Motee in *Star Wars: Episode III* and Chloe in *Home And Away*?
8. Whom did Minnie Caldwell nickname Sunny Jim?
9. Which Weatherfield corner shop proprietor was played by Milton Johns?
10. In which soap does Barbara Young play Sadie Hargreaves?

ANSWERS

1. Blaisdel 2. Arthur Hailey 3. Ashley Peacock 4. *Footballers' Wives* 5. *Quadrophenia* 6. Bev 7. Kristy Wright 8. Jed Stone 9. Brendan Scott 10. *Family Affairs*

QUIZ 166

1 What connects the soap deaths of Len Fairclough, Deon Brennan and Richard Hillman?

2 Which actor connects the roles of Tony Carpenter in *EastEnders* and Antony Moeketsi in *Emmerdale*?

3 What connects the *Coronation Street* actors Liz McDonald and June Dewhurst?

4 Which *Dallas* character connects the surnames Farlow, Ewing and Southworth?

5 In *Coronation Street* what connects the actors John Heanus, Mark Duncan and David Lonsdale?

6 What is the Weatherfield connection between Les Clegg, Alf Roberts, Florrie Lindley and Dev Alahan?

7 Which character in *Dynasty* has been played by both Jack Coleman and Al Corley?

8 What connects the deaths of Val Barlow in *Coronation Street* and Assumpta in *Ballykissangel*?

9 Which surname connects the *Hollyoaks* family of Max, Jude, Gordon and Dawn?

10 What connects the *EastEnders* characters Dirty Den, Eddie Royle, Phil Mitchell and Alfie Moon?

ANSWERS

1. Car crashes 2. Oscar James 3. Both played by Beverley Callard 4. All surnames of Miss Ellie 5. Three of the actors who have played Peter Barlow 6. All owners of the corner shop 7. Steve Carrington 8. Both were electrocuted 9. Cunningham 10. All landlords of the Queen Vic

QUIZ 167

1. Which employee of *Holby City's* General Hospital lost his children in a house fire?
2. In which series did Sarah Lancashire play a teacher called Rachel Jones?
3. In which 1980s soap did Cornelius Garrett play a Covent Garden designer called Alan Stone?
4. Which son of Chastity Dingle is played by Danny Webb?
5. In which decade did Grace Archer die?
6. In *Dynasty*, which singer is the illegitimate daughter of Tom Carrington?
7. Which character played by Terri Dwyer returned to *Hollyoaks* in 2003?
8. In *Emmerdale*, which member of the Dingle family left Luke McCallister standing at the altar?
9. Which star of the soap *Dynasty* was born Roy Scherer?
10. Who played the lead role of Lili in the soap mini-series *Lace*?

ANSWERS

1. Josh Griffiths 2. *Birthday Girl* 3. *Gems* 4. Aaron 5. 1950s 6. Dominique Devereaux 7. Ruth Osborne 8. Tina Dingle 9. Rock Hudson 10. Phoebe Cates

QUIZ 168

1 Which *Neighbours* character was imprisoned for robbing the Kennedy's home?

2 In which city did Pamela and Bobby Ewing tie the knot?

3 Who played Lady Ryder in *Brideshead Revisited*?

4 Who did Weatherfield killer Richard Hillman attempt to frame for the murder of Maxine Peacock?

5 Which star of the sitcom *On The Buses* played the role of Aunt Sal in *EastEnders*?

6 Which emperor was played by Christopher Biggins in *I Claudius*?

7 What is Maria Sutherland's job in *Coronation Street*?

8 In *Edward And Mrs Simpson*, which queen was played by Peggy Ashcroft?

9 Which character, played by Kevin Harrington, returned to *Neighbours* in 2003?

10 Who played the role of Sharon Bentley in *Coronation Street*?

ANSWERS

1. Darcy Tyler 2. New Orleans 3. Claire Bloom 4. Ade Critchley 5. Anna Karen 6. Nero 7. Hairdresser 8. Queen Mary 9. David Bishop 10. Tracie Bennett

QUIZ 169

1. Which was the first Australian soap to be screened on British TV?
2. Which was the first British soap to have its episodes repeated in a weekend omnibus edition?
3. Which was the first British soap to feature the birth of a test-tube baby?
4. Which *Coronation Street* stalwart was the first soap star to receive an honour from the Queen?
5. In which year was *Neighbours* screened for the first time on Australian TV?
6. Who broke the window of the Queen Vic in the very first episode of *EastEnders*?
7. Which animal provides the first name of the character played by Nicola Duffett in *Hollyoaks*?
8. Which character was the reluctant recipient of the first gay kiss to feature in *Coronation Street*?
9. Who was the first character to die in *Brookside*?
10. Which character spoke the very first line in *Coronation Street*?

ANSWERS

1. *The Sullivans* 2. *Brookside* 3. *Crossroads* 4. Violet Carson 5. 1985 6. Nick Cotton 7. Cat 8. Nick Tilsley 9. Gavin Taylor 10. Elsie Lappin

QUIZ 170

1. Who was the best man at the Weatherfield wedding of Des Barnes and Natalie Horrocks?
2. In which country was the fly on the wall docu-soap *Sylvania Waters* set?
3. In which series does Nathan Constance play the role of Josh Mitchell?
4. What was the nickname of fireman Rob Sharpe in *London's Burning*?
5. In which township is Walnut Grove in *The Little House On The Prairie*?
6. In which country had Dirty Den been living following his assumed murder?
7. Who is the real life older brother of *Neighbours* star Stephanie McIntosh?
8. Which soap featured a company called Helios Foods?
9. Which teenager plays the teenager Candice Stowe in *Coronation Street*?
10. Which soap saw the death of Lewis Richardson?

ANSWERS

1. Les Battersby 2. Australia 3. *Bad Girls* 4. Hyper 5. Plumb Creek 6. Spain 7. Jason Donovan 8. *Falcon Crest* 9. Nikki Sanderson 10. *Hollyoaks*

QUIZ 171

1. In *Prisoner Cell Block H* what was the three-letter nickname of the convict Jeannie Brooks?
2. What is Alec Gilroy's favourite tipple in the Rovers Return?
3. Who plays the role of Nicola Blackstock in *Emmerdale*?
4. What is the link between Tommy Nelson in *Coronation Street* and Stuart Parker in *Neighbours*?
5. Who played the role of Edward Ryder in *Brideshead Revisited*?
6. What is Tony Hutchinson's job in *Hollyoaks*?
7. Who played the *Falcon Crest* beauty Jordan Roberts?
8. Which former *Coronation Street* actor starred in the Channel 4 drama *Shameless* in 2004?
9. Who played the role of DS Roz Kelly having previously starred in *Brookside*?
10. How are Seb Miller and Donald Fisher related in *Home And Away*?

ANSWERS

1. Mum 2. Irish whiskey 3. Nicola Wheeler 4. Both car mechanics 5. John Gielgud 6. Chef 7. Morgan Fairchild 8. Chris Bisson 9 .Claire Sweeney 10. Grandson and grandfather

QUIZ 172

1. In which fictional Melbourne suburb is *Neighbours* set?
2. What is the name of Jason Donovan's father, who played the role of Doug Willis in *Neighbours*?
3. Who played the role of Henry Ramsay?
4. What is the name of the business complex in *Neighbours*, that boasts a hotel, coffee shop, a pub and a hairdresser's?
5. What was the name of Mrs Mangel's husband?
6. Which *Neighbours* character dropped out of a university engineering course to become an airline steward?
7. What was the name of Harold Bishop's wife?
8. Cheryl, Danni and Brett are all members of which *Neighbours* family?
9. Who created the show?
10. Who sings the *Neighbours* theme?

ANSWERS

1. Erinsborough 2. Terence Donovan 3. Craig McLachlan 4. Lassiters 5. Len 6. Paul Robinson 7. Madge 8. The Starks 9. Reg Watson 10. Barry Crocker

QUIZ 173

1. What is the soap link between Morgan Fairchild, Priscilla Presley and Francine Tacker?
2. Which pop group made a cameo appearance in *Crossroads* in 2001?
3. Which star of the soap *Falcon Crest* was born Sarah Jane Faulks?
4. What was the name of the pub owned by Fraser Henderson in *Coronation Street*?
5. Who was the best man at the 2003 *Neighbours* wedding of Dee and Toadie?
6. Mary Ellen, Jason, Erin, John Boy, Jim Bob, Ben and Elizabeth are the children of which family?
7. What was John Watts rank in *Z Cars*?
8. What is the first name of the *Emmerdale* character whose surnames have been Oakwell, Thornfield and Cockburn?
9. In which soap was the character of Big Ron often seen drinking at the bar?
10. In which Florida county was *Flamingo Road* set?

ANSWERS

1. All played Jenna Wade in *Dallas* 2. Steps 3. Jane Wyman 4. The Hour Glass 5. Stonefish Rebecchi 6. The Waltons 7. Detective Sergeant 8. Tara 9. *EastEnders* 10. Truro County

QUIZ 174

1. What is the name of the character played by Deena Payne in *Emmerdale*?
2. Aboard which ship did Lady Marjorie die in *Upstairs Downstairs*?
3. Which star of *The Colbys* was born John Carter?
4. How was Esther related to John Boy in *The Waltons*?
5. Who did Gunther Meisner play in the mini-soap *The Winds Of War*?
6. Who plays the role of Samantha Jones in *Sex And The City*?
7. Was the soap actor Ross Kemp born in 1964, 1965 or 1966?
8. Which character was the bridegroom in the pilot episode of *Dynasty*?
9. Which star of the soap *Dallas* was born Howard Leek?
10. Who played Les Baxter in the US soap *All My Children*, but is better known for his role in *Starsky And Hutch*?

ANSWERS

1. Viv Hope 2. *Titanic* 3. Charlton Heston 4. Grandmother and grandson 5. Hitler 6. Kim Cattrall 7. 1964 8. Blake Carrington 9. Howard Keel 10. Antonio Fargas

QUIZ 175

In each group of four, which character is from a different soap?

1. In *Coronation Street*: Geena Gregory, Dennis Tanner, Peggy Sagar, Ted Sullivan
2. In *EastEnders*: Alex Healy, Bert Duggan, Roy Evans, Mo Harris
3. In *Hollyoaks*: Pacey Witter, Kurt Benson, Jasmine Bates, Toby Mills
4. In *Dallas*: Valene Ewing, Mitch Cooper, Ray Krebbs, Robin Agretti
5. In *Dynasty*: Javier Fernandez, King Galen, Andrew Laird, Rudy Richards
6. In *Emmerdale*: Edna Birch, Sam Curtis, Biff Fowler, Chloe Atkinson
7. In *Neighbours*: Darcy Tyler, Blake Dean, Joe Scully, Gaby Willis
8. In *Brookside*: Bel Simpson, Marty Murray, Andrew Kerr, Karen Grant
9. In *Crossroads*: Betty Waddell, Mandy Dobbs, Oona Stocks, Sean McCallister
10. In *Holby City*: Ben Saunders, Diane Leeds, Danny Shaughnessy, Jess Griffin

ANSWERS

1. Peggy Sagar from *Albion Market* 2. Bert Duggan from *The Sullivans* 3. Pacey Witter from *Dawson's Creek* 4. Robin Agretti from *Falcon Crest* 5. Javier Fernandez from *Eldorado* 6. Sam Curtis from *Flamingo Road* 7. Blake Dean from *Home And Away* 8. Andrew Kerr from *The Newcomers* 9. Sean McCallister from *The Colbys* 10. Diane Leeds from *ER*

QUIZ 176

1 On whose novel was the mini-series *Hollywood Wives* set?

2 Which *EastEnders* star played the role of Gladys in the 2003 comedy drama *Margery And Gladys*?

3 In which year did the family from hell, the Battersbys, move to *Coronation Street*?

4 Who played the lawyer Victor Sufuentes in *LA Law*?

5 Which series sees Robert Carlyle patrolling the village of Lochdubh?

6 Which star of *Emmerdale* went on to play the role of Rebecca Patterson in *Fat Friends*?

7 What is the title of the US series that began in 2003 and is set at the Montecito Resort and Casino?

8 Who played the role of Albert Dingle in *Emmerdale* and Ron Sykes in *Coronation Street*?

9 On whose novel was the soap mini-series *Princess Daisy* set?

10 In which city is the US series *Beacon Hill* set?

ANSWERS

1. Jackie Collins 2. June Brown 3. 1997 4. Jimmy Smits 5. Hamish Macbeth 6. Lisa Riley 7. Las Vegas 8. Bobby Knutt 9. Judith Krantz 10. Boston

QUIZ 177

1. In *Coronation Street* what is Kevin Webster's sister called?
2. Who left Walford in 1997 and went on to play PC Sydenham in *City Central*?
3. In which British medical soap does Michael Kitchen play Jack Turner?
4. Which US medical soap features the character of Dr Jack McNeil?
5. Which former model plays the role of Stephanie Stokes in *Emmerdale*?
6. Who played Fiona Brake in *Night And Day* having previously starred in the crime series *Dempsey And Makepeace*?
7. Which future Hollywood heart throb played the role of Mason Capwell in the 1980s soap *Santa Barbara*?
8. The US series *Nip/Tuck* is set in which city?
9. In which soap was Karen Travers sent to jail for stabbing her husband to death?
10. Peter Horton played Professor Gary Shepherd in which US series?

ANSWERS

1. Debbie 2. Paul Nicholls 3. *A & E* 4. Chicago Hope 5. Lorraine Chase 6. Glynnis Barber 7. Leonardo DiCaprio 8. Miami 9. *Prisoner Cell Block H* 10. *Thirtysomething*

QUIZ 178

1. What is the name of the regiment that features in *Soldier Soldier*?
2. What was the surname of the character played by Robson Green in the series?
3. What was the surname of the character played by Jerome Flynn in the series?
4. In which year did the series begin?
5. In which stage show did Jerome Flynn later play Tommy Cooper?
6. Who created the show *Soldier Soldier*?
7. What nickname was given to the *Soldier Soldier* character of Eddie Nelson?
8. Which song, previously a hit for the Righteous Brothers, topped the charts for Robson and Jerome?
9. Who played the role of Lieutenant Colonel Dan Fortune?
10. Who is the older, Robson Green or Jerome Flynn?

ANSWERS

1. King's Own Fusiliers 2. Tucker 3. Garvey 4. 1991 5. *Jus' Like That* 6. Lucy Gannon 7. Horatio 8. 'Unchained Melody' 9. Miles Anderson 10. Jerome Flynn (by nine months)

QUIZ 179

1. Who links the roles of Pauline Robson in *Brookside* and Marilyn Fenner in *Bad Girls*?
2. In *Dynasty*, King Galen was king of where?
3. Who played the role of Jack Walker in the early days of *Coronation Street*?
4. In which mini-series did the soap star Joan Collins play Helen Junot?
5. Which Weatherfield character has owned the Kabin for the greatest number of years?
6. In which US soap did Jo Reynolds kill a drug smuggler called Reed Carter?
7. Which star of *Emmerdale* played Sergeant Len Able in *Carry On England*?
8. Which British movie star joined the cast of *EastEnders* in 2001 as Margaret Walker?
9. In which year was the final episode of *Albion Market* screened?
10. Which rock star joined the cast of *Ally McBeal* in 2002 playing the role of Victor Morrison?

ANSWERS

1. Kim Taylforth 2. Moldavia 3. Arthur Leslie 4. Sins 5. Rita Sullivan 6. *Melrose Place* 7. Patrick Mower 8. Susan George 9. 1986 10. Jon Bon Jovi

QUIZ 180

1 In *Dynasty.* which bride's wedding was interrupted by machine gun toting revolutionaries?

2 Which *Coronation Street* star went on to play Sam Docherty in *A & E*?

3 Who did Dr Fonsenca replace in *EastEnders*?

4 Who stood as the Alf Roberts' mayoress in 1973?

5 Which series used as its theme music 'Spartacus' by Khachaturyan?

6 Which pop superstar has played the soap roles of Carla, Robin and Charlene?

7 In 2004 who left Ciaran standing at the altar in *Coronation Street*?

8 In which short-lived 1970s soap did Norman Beaton play Everton, the head of the Bennett family?

9 On what train did Angie and Dennis Watts return from their second honeymoon?

10 In which city is the US soap *Central Park West* set?

ANSWERS

1. Amanda Carrington 2. Jane Danson 3. Dr Legg 4. Annie Walker 5. *The Onedin Line* 6. Kylie Minogue 7. Sunita Parekh 8. *Empire Road* 9. The *Orient Express* 10. New York

QUIZ 181

Name the actors who have played the following roles in *EastEnders*.

1 Charlie Cotton
2 Melanie Healy
3 Patrick Trueman
4 Trevor Short
5 Diane Butcher
6 Zoe Slater
7 Debbie Wilkins
8 Jim Branning
9 James Wilmot Brown
10 Angel

ANSWERS

1. Christopher Hancock 2. Tamzin Outhwaite 3. Rudolph Walker 4. Phil McDermott 5. Sophie Lawrence 6. Michelle Ryan 7. Shirley Cheriton 8. John Bardon 9. William Boyde 10. Goldie

QUIZ 182

1. In *Coronation Street,* what is the name of the younger brother of Des Barnes?
2. What make of car connects Inspector Morse and Mike Baldwin?
3. In which year did *Footballers' Wives* make its TV debut?
4. In which US state is the series *Picket Fences* set?
5. Which *Coronation Street* favourite went on to play Mrs Ashburn in *Fat Friends*?
6. Who played the role of Goose in the film *Top Gun*, before joining the cast of *ER* as a doctor?
7. In *EastEnders* what surname links the characters of Naima and Saeed?
8. In which series did Sarah Lancashire play the role of Yvonne Kolakowski?
9. On whose novels were the mini-series *The Glass Virgin* and *The Tide Of Life* based?
10. Which member of the Mangel family in *Neighbours* was played by Finn Greentree Keene?

ANSWERS

1. Colin 2. *Jaguar* 3. 2002 4. Wisconsin 5. Thelma Barlow 6. Anthony Edwards 7. Jeffrey 8. *Clocking Off* 9. Catherine Cookson 10. Toby Mangel

QUIZ 183

1. In which year did the character of Alfie Moon first appear in *EastEnders*?
2. In *Dawson's Creek*, what is the name of Dawson's little sister?
3. In *Coronation Street*, what type of shop was managed by Peter Barlow?
4. In *EastEnders*, which country did Lisa Fowler flee to with her baby, only to be tracked down by Phil Mitchell?
5. What was Lisa Duckworth's maiden name before her marriage to Terry Duckworth?
6. Which *Emmerdale* rogues attempted to rob Zoe Tate in December 2003?
7. Which song, a hit for the ex-*Neighbours* star Kylie Minogue, was originally a hit for Little Eva?
8. What is Audrey Roberts favourite tipple in the Rovers Return?
9. Which character in *Cold Feet* was killed in a car crash in the final series?
10. Whom did Curly Watts name a star after?

ANSWERS

1. 2002 2. Lily 3. A bookmaker's 4. Portugal 5. Lisa Horton 6. The Dingles 7. 'The Locomotion' 8. Gin and tonic 9. Rachel Bradley 10. His bride to be, Raquel

QUIZ 184

Name the actors who have played the following characters in *Coronation Street.*

1 Tanya Pooley
2 Steve McDonald
3 Fiz Brown
4 Duggie Ferguson
5 Todd Grimshaw
6 Archie Shuttleworth
7 Spider Nugent
8 Andy McDonald
9 Jerry Booth
10 Toyah Battersby

ANSWERS

1. Eva Pope 2. Simon Gregson 3. Jennie McAlpine 4. John Bowe 5. Bruno Langley 6. Roy Hudd 7. Martin Hancock 8. Nicholas Cochrane 9. Graham Haberfield 10. Georgia Taylor

QUIZ 185

1. What is the name of Cilla Brown's son in *Coronation Street*?
2. In which English county is the series *Harbour Lights* set?
3. Who links the roles of Hayley in *Coronation Street* and Rose in *The Dwelling Place*?
4. *War And Remembrance* was a sequel to which soap mini-series?
5. Who won a penny bet for managing to lure Roy Cropper into bed?
6. In which series did Cass Rickman fall victim to the Sun Hill serial killer?
7. Which was the first British soap to be filmed inside real houses?
8. In which city did Inspector Morse do his detecting?
9. Which soap opera star went on to record an album entitled *Ten Good Reasons*?
10. In 2001, Julie Goodyear was appointed as an ambassador to which city?

ANSWERS

1. Chesney 2. Dorset 3. Julie Hesmondhalgh 4. *The Winds Of War* 5. Tracy Barlow 6. *The Bill* 7. *Brookside* 8. Oxford 9. Jason Donovan 10. Liverpool

QUIZ 186

1 Who played the title role in Perry Mason?

2 Who played the wife of Sid James in *Bless This House* and went on to play the role of Marion Terson in *Triangle*?

3 Which character left *The Bill* after being accidently shot by PC Dale Smith?

4 When Dirty Den was shot in 1990, what type of flowers did the gunman hide his weapon behind?

5 Which star of *Dynasty* was born John Lincoln Freund?

6 In the opening credits of *Coronation Street*, what type of animal is seen settling down to sleep?

7 In which year was the last episode of *Dallas* screened?

8 In *Dynasty*, which member of the Carrington family was revealed as a homosexual?

9 At Christmas 1996, which *Brookside* character's house was the subject of an arson attack?

10 Does the postbox on *Coronation Street* stand outside the Kabin, the corner shop or the Rovers Return?

ANSWERS

1. Raymond Burr 2. Diana Coupland 3. Sergeant Bob Cryer 4. Daffodils 5. John Forsythe 6. A cat 7. 1991 8. Steven Carrington 9. Ron Dixon 10. The corner shop

QUIZ 187

1. What is the nationality of *The Bill*'s CID officer Duncan Lennox?
2. Who created *The Bill*?
3. Which Sun Hill Superintendent was played by Peter Ellis?
4. Who played the role of PC Garfield in *The Bill*?
5. Which *EastEnders* regular played a gangster called Jimmy Smith in *The Bill*?
6. Which French football star made a guest appearance as himself in *The Bill*, in December 1998?
7. What is Sergeant Boyden's first name?
8. Which PC was played by Andrew Paul?
9. Who left Sun Hill after accusing PC Santini of sexual harrassment, to later return as a detective sergeant?
10. Which Chief Inspector of Sun Hill Station was portrayed by Ben Roberts?

ANSWERS

1. Scottish 2. Geoff McQueen 3. Superintendent Brownlow 4. Huw Higginson 5. Leslie Grantham 6. Emmanuel Petit 7. Matthew or Matt 8. PC Quinnan 9. Rosie Fox 10. Derek Conway

QUIZ 188

1 Who has played Jasmine in *Holby City*, Darcey in *Cutting It* and Fiona in *Coronation Street*?

2 In which soap was a cook called Mrs Cornet killed in an explosion?

3 Was the soap actor Todd Carty born in 1961, 1962 or 1963?

4 Which soap character owned a business called Pam's Aerobics Unlimited?

5 What is the name of the local pub in *The Archers*?

6 Which Weatherfield character has been romantically involved with Maggie, Bet, Deidre, Suzie, Susan, Alma and Jackie?

7 Which soap has broadcast special editions entitled *Indecent Behaviour* and *Leap Of Faith*?

8 Who played the role of Neely in *Baywatch*?

9 Which 1960s series featured three brothers called Jarrod, Nick and Heath?

10 In which year of the 1980s was the last episode of *St Elsewhere* made?

ANSWERS

1. Angela Griffin 2. *Crossroads* 3. 1963 4. Pamela Ewing 5. The Bull 6. Mike Baldwin 7. *Hollyoaks* 8. Gina Lee Nolin 9. *The Big Valley* 10. 1988

QUIZ 189

1. In which city is *Taggart* set?
2. What type of animal was Pete, Elizabeth Walton's pet?
3. In which series does former *EastEnders* star Nick Berry play an undercover cop called Liam Ketman?
4. *Trapper John* was a spin off from which long-running series?
5. After which *Neighbours* resident was Ramsay Street named?
6. What was the title of the 1982 spin off from *The Little House On The Prairie*?
7. Who returned to Walford in 2002, to discover his sister dining on dog food?
8. Which US soap has broadcast episodes entitled *Tamara's Return* and *Capeside Revisited*?
9. Which *ER* doctor was diagnozed with a brain tumour?
10. Which star of the TV shows *I Claudius* and *Porridge* played himself in several episodes of *Bad Girls*?

ANSWERS

1. Glasgow 2. Raccoon 3. *In Deep* 4. *M.A.S.H.* 5. Jack Ramsay 6. *The Little House: A New Beginning* 7. Ricky Butcher 8. *Dawson's Creek* 9. Dr Mark Greene 10. Christopher Biggins

QUIZ 190

1. When *Heartbeat* began in 1992, in which year of the 1960s was it set?
2. Which niece of Walter Matthau played the role of Jo Weston in *Heartbeat*?
3. What is the name of the police station in Aidensfield?
4. Which Aidensfield doctor died in a house fire on Green End Terrace?
5. What type of shop did Sergeant Blaketon run after retiring from the force due to ill health?
6. Jo Weston was the second wife of which *Heartbeat* character?
7. Which lovable rogue is played by Bill Maynard in the series?
8. Which Aidensfield Arms barmaid is played by Tricia Penrose?
9. What disease claimed the life of Kate Rowan?
10. Which star of *The Darling Buds Of May* played the role of Sergeant Craddock in *Heartbeat*?

ANSWERS

1. 1964 2. Juliette Gruber 3. Ashfordly Police Station 4. Dr Neil Bolton 5. Post Office 6. PC Nick Rowan 7. Claude Greengrass 8. Gina Ward 9. Leukemia 10. Philip Franks

QUIZ 191

1. In which series did Lenny Henry play a head teacher called Ian George?
2. Which surname is shared by Pete, Ian and Laura in *EastEnders*?
3. In *Neighbours* which member of the Stark family struck it rich after winning the lottery?
4. The *Dynasty* character Mark Jennings pursued a career in which sport?
5. Which scriptwriter for *Brookside* went on to create *Cracker*?
6. In which soap did Travis Nash date Donna Bishop?
7. In which soap were the characters of Finn and Comfort involved in a major rail crash?
8. Which *Neighbours* star went on to become the face of L'Oreal?
9. What is the title of the series in which former *EastEnders* star Ross Kemp plays a lawyer called Sam Lucas?
10. Which member of the Sullivan family was played by William Maxwell in *Brookside*?

ANSWERS

1. *Hope And Glory* 2. Beale 3. Cheryl Stark 4. Tennis 5. Jimmy McGovern 6. *Home And Away* 7. *Casualty* 8. Natalie Imbruglia 9. *In Defence* 10. Jack Sullivan

QUIZ 192

1 Who played Jan Glover in *Emmerdale* and Wendy Crosier in *Coronation Street*?

2 In *The Big Valley*, was the Barkley's ranch servant called Sam, Silas or Spencer?

3 In what year did the villainous Steve Owen turn up in Albert Square?

4 Which *Dynasty* character was the son of the Carrington's butler, Joseph?

5 Who installed the faulty electric wiring in the Rovers Return cellar that caused the pub fire?

6 In which decade is *The Jewel In The Crown* set?

7 Which US soap featured a coffee shop called The Hot Biscuit?

8 Which British soap is set on Thornton Street?

9 Which Channel 4 series includes in its cast a cute dog called Mitzy?

10 In which soap has sports presenter Des Lynam appeared as himself?

ANSWERS

1. Roberta Kerr 2. Silas 3. 1998 4. Sean Anders Rowan 5. Jack Duckworth 6. 1940s 7. *Dallas* 8. *Night And Day* 9. *Hollyoaks* 10. *Footballers' Wives*

QUIZ 193

Who is the older of each Weatherfield pair?

1 Ken Barlow or Rita Sullivan
2 Curly Watts or Martin Platt
3 Ena Sharples or Minnie Caldwell
4 Eddie Yeats or Bet Lynch
5 Elsie Tanner or Len Fairclough
6 Deidre Rachid or Roy Cropper
7 Kevin Webster or Terry Duckworth
8 Hilda Ogden or Emily Bishop
9 Pery Sugden or Stan Ogden
10 Mike Baldwin or Vera Duckworth

ANSWERS

1. Rita born 1932 (Ken born 1939) 2. Curly born 1964 (Martin born 1968) 3. Ena born 1899 (Minnie born 1900) 4. Bet born 1940 (Eddie born 1941) 5. Elsie born 1923 (Len born 1924) 6. Roy born 1954 (Deidre born 1955) 7. Terry born 1964 (Kevin born 1965) 8. Hilda born 1924 (Emily born 1929) 9. Stan born 1919 (Percy born 1922) 10. Vera born 1937 (Mike born 1942)

QUIZ 194

1. In *Neighbours*, what is Toadie's small white dog called?
2. In which county is *Hollyoaks* set?
3. In which year did soap actress Pat Phoenix die?
4. Which of The Waltons' children was played by Eric Scott. Was it Jim Bob, Jason or Ben?
5. How did Roly the dog die in *EastEnders*?
6. Which 1950s, soap set in Hendon, starred Christopher Beeny and is widely recognized as being the BBC's first soap?
7. In *Neighbours,* which dog did Bouncer marry in a surreal dream sequence?
8. Did Des Barnes first appear in *Coronation Street* in 1989, 1990 or 1991?
9. What is Nisha Batra's job in *Brookside*?
10. Which was the first *Coronation Street* family to own a colour television?

ANSWERS

1. Bob 2. Cheshire 3. 1986 4. Ben 5. Hit by a car 6. *The Grove Family* 7. Rosie 8. 1991 9. Nurse 10. The Ogdens

QUIZ 195

1 Which actress spoke the line "Crossroads Motel, may I help you?", the first-ever line spoken in the soap?

2 Which R is the name of a neighbouring village of *Emmerdale*?

3 Which series features a character nicknamed Body Bag?

4 What is the first name of Jessica Tate's younger sister in *Soap*?

5 Molly Sugden played Nellie Harvey, the landlady of which Weatherfield pub?

6 Did JR Ewing generally wear a trilby, a baseball cap or a stetson?

7 Who has played the roles of Pam in *Holby City*, Marsha in *Soldier Soldier* and Natalie in *Coronation Street*?

8 Who bought Tracy Barlow a house for the Christmas of 2003?

9 Which US soap featured a company called Lex-Dex?

10 Which of the following characters has Curly Watts not slept with? Is it Maureen, Deidre or Raquel?

ANSWERS

1. Jane Rossington 2. Robblesfield 3. *Bad Girls* 4. Mary 5. The Laughing Donkey 6. Stetson 7. Denise Welch 8. Her grandmother, Blanche Hunt 9. *Dynasty* 10. Deidre

QUIZ 196

In *Coronation Street* …

1 Who played the role of pub landlady Annie Walker?
2 Which brewery supplies the Rovers Return?
3 Whom did Hilda Ogden replace as the cleaner of the Rovers?
4 At the beginning of the 21st century who lived next door to the Rovers?
5 Which popular bar maid, and later landlady, owns over 250 pairs of earrings?
6 In which year of the 1990s did Vera and Jack Duckworth take over the Rovers?
7 Why was the Rovers Return closed for three months in 1986?
8 Who is the longest-serving barmaid at the Rovers?
9 Who was appointed by the brewery as the Rovers Return pot man in 1975?
10 Which Rovers Return landlord died of a heart attack in 1970?

ANSWERS

1. Doris Speed 2. Newton and Ridley 3. Martha Longhurst 4. Ken Barlow 5. Bet Lynch 6. 1995 7. It was gutted by fire 8. Betty Williams (or Turpin) 9. Fred Gee 10. Jack Walker

QUIZ 197

1 What was the name of the Tavernier family's genial grandfather in *EastEnders*?

2 In which year did Zoe and Little Mo Slater appear in *EastEnders*?

3 Which Scottish soap is set on Montego Street?

4 In which series did Pam Ferris and Keith Barron play man and wife, Pat and Roy Fletcher?

5 What type of vehicle does the soap character Josh Griffiths usually drive?

6 In which soap did Mick Johnson own a shop called The Pizza Parlour?

7 In which country is the series *Hearts Of Gold* set?

8 Which soap star was born Shane Patrick Roche?

9 What connects the *EastEnders* characters Colin Russell and Derek Harkinson?

10 Which actor joined the cast of *Neighbours* after finishing runner-up in the Australian version of *Big Brother*?

ANSWERS

1. Jules 2. 2000 3. River City 4. *Clocking Off* 5. An ambulance in *Casualty* 6. *Brookside* 7. Wales 8. Shane Richie 9. They are both gay 10. Blair McDonough

QUIZ 198

1. Who plays the role of Jerry Walsh in *Doctors*?
2. In 1998, which *Coronation Street* character worked as a nude model?
3. Which actor, Oscar nominated for his role in Chaplin, played the lawyer Larry Paul in *Ally McBeal*?
4. What is the name of the character played by Claire King in *Bad Girls*?
5. What was Charlene Mitchell's job in *Neighbours*?
6. What was Brady Lloyd's job in *Dynasty*?
7. Which Australian soap featured the formidable character of Sister Jeffries?
8. In which soap were the characters of Roy and Fern Farmer killed off in 2003?
9. Harold and Calico were both names of what in *The Waltons*?
10. Who plays the role of Jenny Gifford in *Cold Feet*?

ANSWERS

1. Guy Burgess 2. Nick Tilsley 3. Robert Downey Jnr 4. Karen Betts 5. Car mechanic 6. Record company executive 7. *The Young Doctors* 8. *Hollyoaks* 9. Cats 10. Fay Ripley

QUIZ 199

Unravel the anagrams to give the names of actors from *Dallas* and *Dynasty*.

1 From *Dallas* A LADY GRIN

2 From *Dynasty* SANDAL VEIN

3 From *Dallas* ONE DARNED

4 From *Dynasty* SHOCK ROUND

5 From *Dallas* WORK HEALED

6 From *Dynasty* MAMMA MESS

7 From *Dallas* RIP SPILLS A CELERY

8 From *Dynasty* MAGICAL WAR

9 From *Dallas* PICKY TURF FAD

10 From *Dynasty* EAT A KORMA

ANSWERS

1. Linda Gray 2. Linda Evans 3. Donna Reed 4. Rock Hudson 5. Howard Keel 6. Emma Samms 7. Priscilla Presley 8. Ali MacGraw 9. Patrick Duffy 10. Kate O'Mara

QUIZ 200

1. In which legal drama did former *Coronation Street* star Sarah Lancashire play a QC called Anne Cloves?
2. Who plays the role of Louise Appleton in *Emmerdale*?
3. Who played Debbie in the *Brookside* spin-off *Damon And Debbie*?
4. What is Arthur Bright's occupation in *Neighbours*?
5. Who played the role of Governor Picker in the 1998 film *Primary Colors*, after starring for many years in *Dallas*?
6. Which member of The Beatles played the role of Robin Valerian in the soap mini-series *Princess Daisy*?
7. Which Weatherfield conman was played by Owen Aaronovitch?
8. Which series co-starred Leslie Grantham and Anita Dobson as Terry and Sam Greene?
9. Who joined the cast of *Ballykissangel* following the death of her father Tony Doyle?
10. Which soap featured a chef called Gerald Lovejoy?

ANSWERS

1. *Verdict* 2. Emily Symons 3. Gillian Kearney 4. Undertaker 5. Larry Hagman 6. Ringo Starr 7. Jon Lindsay 8. *The Stretch* 9. Susannah Doyle 10. *Crossroads*

QUIZ 201

1. Who plays the role of Tommy Harris in *Coronation Street*?
2. What was Maggie Channing's maiden name in *Falcon Crest*?
3. In *Coronation Street*, what type of business did Jim McDonald open in premises under the viaduct?
4. In which country is the soap *River City* set?
5. Is Monica Colby a blonde, a brunette or a redhead?
6. How many times has Elsie Tanner married in *Coronation Street*?
7. Which soap star penned an autobiography entitled *Past Imperfect*?
8. Which was the first UK soap to be screened five days a week?
9. Which US soap featured a fashion company called Fashion Fury?
10. In which series was Dr David Shearer killed in a car crash?

ANSWERS

1. Thomas Craig 2. Maggie Gioberti 3. A motorcycle repair shop 4. Scotland 5. Brunette 6. Three 7. Joan Collins 8. *Crossroads* 9. *Dynasty* 10. *Peak Practice*

QUIZ 202

In *Coronation Street* who died in...

1. October 1997 after crashing a car into the viaduct?
2. January 2002 after crashing a taxi cab?
3. February 1989 after being stabbed outside a nightclub?
4. January 1978 after being shot in a wages snatch?
5. November 1998 after being attacked by a gang of drug dealers?
6. July 1980 after a car crash on a driving lesson?
7. May 1964 after a heart attack in the Rovers Return snug?
8. December 1983 after a motorway crash?
9. October 1998 after being locked inside a Frescho's freezer?
10. December 1997 after being run over by Les Battersby?

ANSWERS

1. Don Brennan 2. Dennis Stringer 3. Brian Tilsley 4. Ernest Bishop 5. Des Barnes 6. Renee Roberts 7. Martha Longhurst 8. Len Fairclough 9. Anne Malone 10. Theresa the turkey

QUIZ 203

1. What do the initials *ER* stand for with regard to the medical soap?
2. In *Casualty* what nickname was given to the porter Derek Sunderland?
3. What is the name of Chrissy Costello's daughter in *Family Affairs*, whom Chrissy claimed was suffering from cancer?
4. Who played the role of Sinbad in *Brookside*?
5. In which Scottish village did Sam Mitchell marry Ricky Butcher?
6. Who played Nurse Carol in *Albion Market* and went on to play the wife of Ian Beale?
7. Which soap won the Best Serial Drama Award at the 2002 National TV Awards?
8. Which celebrity chef had a cameo role in *Hollyoaks* in 2003?
9. What was Peter Montague's job in *Brookside*?
10. On whose novel was the soap mini-series *East Of Eden* set?

ANSWERS

1. Emergency Room 2. Sunny 3. Chloe 4. Michael Starke 5. Gretna Green 6. Michelle Collins 7. *Emmerdale* 8. Kevin Woodford 9. Teacher 10. John Steinbeck

QUIZ 204

1 Which TV soap's theme music is entitled 'Kaleidoscope No 21'?

2 Which member of the Dingle clan slept with his cousin Charity?

3 In *The Bill* which PC, played by Michael Higgs, was shot dead in his own flat?

4 Which series starring Michelle Collins is set on the Scottish island of Ronansay?

5 Sadie, Gary and Trish McDonald have all featured in which soap?

6 Which soap character had affairs with Marilee Stone and Holly Harwood?

7 In *EastEnders*, whose love interests have included Garry, Anthony, Paul, Alfie and Andy?

8 In *Coronation Street* who had a love affair with a newspaper reporter called Jackie Marsh?

9 In *Emmerdale*, whom did Ted Sharp kidnap in 1989?

10 In *EastEnders* which member of the di Marco family was played by Louise Jameson?

ANSWERS

1. *Coronation Street* 2. Marlon 3. Eddie Santini 4. *Two Thousand Acres of Sky* 5. High Road 6. JR Ewing 7. Kat Moon (nee Slater) 8. Ken Barlow 9. Dolly Skilbeck 10. Rosa

QUIZ 205

In what decade were the following *Coronation Street* stars born?

1 Helen Worth
2 Betty Driver
3 William Roache
4 Sean Wilson
5 Julie Goodyear
6 Doris Speed
7 Bill Ward
8 Liz Dawn
9 Simon Gregson
10 Anne Kirkbride

ANSWERS

1. 1950s 2. 1920s 3. 1930s 4. 1960s 5. 1940s 6. 1890s 7. 1910s 8. 1930s 9. 1970s 10. 1950s

QUIZ 206

1 What kind of animal was Myrtle in *The Waltons*?

2 In *EastEnders*, which member of the Ferreira family is played by Ameet Chana?

3 What was the first name of DS McCallister in *The Bill*?

4 In *Coronation Street*, who has fathered children by Andrea, Lisa and Tricia?

5 Who played the role of Virginia O'Kane in *Bad Girls*?

6 Which soap is filmed on a real-life street called Pin Oak Court?

7 Which *Coronation Street* regular was born Sylvia Butterfield?

8 What job is held by Alex Healy in Walford?

9 Which original Bond girl played the role of Madame Malec in *Falcon Crest*?

10 The Capwells and the Lockridges were rival families in which soap?

ANSWERS

1. A goat 2. Adi 3. Debbie 4. Terry Duckworth 5. Kate O'Mara 6. *Neighbours* 7. Liz Dawn 8. Vicar 9. Ursula Andress 10. *Santa Barbara*

QUIZ 207

1. Who plays the role of Bev Unwin in *Coronation Street*?
2. Which *Crossroads* actress died of cancer in April 1985?
3. Which soap features thoroughfares called Eastham Crescent and Oakhill Drive?
4. Which character in *The Bill* was affectionately known as Uncle Bob?
5. In which county is *Family Affairs* set?
6. In which city was the 1990s US soap *Models Inc* set?
7. Which soap character owned a fast-food van called Mandy's Munchbox?
8. What was Michael Choi's occupation in *Brookside*?
9. Which member of the Ewing clan died in Alaska?
10. Which soap features a hospital called the King George VI Hospital?

ANSWERS

1. Susie Blake 2. Noele Gordon 3. *Hollyoaks* 4. Bob Cryer 5. Kent 6. Los Angeles 7. Mandy Dingle 8. Doctor 9. Jason 10. *EastEnders*

QUIZ 208

What was the surname of the Weatherfield characters who divorced in the given years?

1. Ivan and Linda in 1984
2. Martin and Gail in 2001
3. Mike and Susan in 1988
4. Nick and Leanne in 1999
5. Norris and Angela in 1999
6. Jerry and Myra in 1968
7. Alan and Elsie in 1978
8. Fred and Maureen in 1999
9. Les and Maggie in 1970
10. Bill and Elaine in 1995

ANSWERS

1. Cheveski 2. Platt 3. Baldwin 4. Tilsley 5. Cole 6. Booth 7. Howard 8. Elliott 9. Clegg 10. Webster

QUIZ 209

1. Who plays a QC called Jo Miller in *Judge John Deed*?
2. Which soap town has been served by Dr Summerbee, Dr Merrick and Dr Bolton among others?
3. What is the first name of Dr Dangerfield in *Dangerfield*?
4. Who played the role of Miles Colby in *The Colbys*?
5. Which character in *The Darling Buds Of May* had the catchphrase "perfick"?
6. What connects the people that played Tom Ashby in *Brookside* and Hilda Ogden in *Coronation Street*?
7. Which gossipmonger left Albert Square in 1993 and returned in 1997?
8. What is the first name of PC Carver in *The Bill*?
9. Who has played the roles of Helen in *Emmerdale*, Mags in *EastEnders* and Rose in *Angels*?
10. In which Italian city did Adam and Jill Chance enjoy their honeymoon?

ANSWERS

1. Jenny Seagrove 2. Aidensfield 3. Paul 4. Maxwell Caulfield 5. Pop Larkin 6. Both called Alexander (Peter and Jean) 7. Dot Cotton 8. Jim 9. Katryn Apanowicz 10. Venice

QUIZ 210

• •

1 In *Home And Away*, which teacher was nicknamed Turangela by her pupils?

2 What type of bird was Chirpee, the pet of Grandma Walton?

3 In which year did Kylie Minogue leave *Neighbours* to pursue her pop career?

4 What is Johnno Dean's job in *Hollyoaks*?

5 Which Sun Hill inspector was played by Philip Whitchurch?

6 Who were the bride and groom when an Ogden married a Barlow?

7 In the very first episode of *Brookside*, which family moved into Brookside Close?

8 What is the three-letter nickname of the *Casualty* character John Denham?

9 Who played the role of Aunt Sally in *Worzel Gummidge* and went on to guest as Anthea Cowley in *Heartbeat*?

10 In *EastEnders*, what is the name of Dennis Watts' father?

ANSWERS

1. Angie Russell 2. Canary 3. 1988 4. Long-distance lorry driver 5. Chief Inspector Cato 6. Irma and David 7. The Collins family 8. Abs 9. Una Stubbs 10. Dennis senior

QUIZ 211

In *Emmerdale* …

1 Who became Mrs Jack Sugden in 1994?
2 Which of the Sugden clan lived at Demdyke Cottage?
3 Which daughter of Annie Sugden died of a brain haemorrhage?
4 Who originally played the role of Jack Sugden?
5 What was the name of Annie Sugden's first husband?
6 Whom did Annie Sugden marry in 1993?
7 Which Sugden siblings were killed while crossing a level crossing?
8 Which wife of Jack Sugden was killed in a hit-and-run road accident?
9 Which of the Sugden clan was born in April 1986?
10 What was the title of the best-selling novel that Jack Sugden wrote in 1974?

ANSWERS

1. Sarah Connolly 2. Joe Sugden 3. Peggy 4. Andrew Burt 5. Jacob 6. Leonard Kempinski 7. Sam and Sally 8. Pat Sugden 9. Robert Jacob Sugden 10. *The Field Of Tares*

QUIZ 212

1. Who was made temporary president of Ewing Oil, following the shooting of JR Ewing?
2. What colour is the door of the Rovers Return?
3. Which series took its title from the two words in the phonetic alphabet that represent the letters J and B?
4. In 1995, which series shortened its title to *The Ward*?
5. In which county is *Wycliffe* set?
6. Who played the title role in *Kavanagh QC*?
7. Which actor met his future wife Dee Sadler after rescuing her in an episode of *Casualty*?
8. According to the title of a 1980s series, on which street did Elisabeth Moulton-Barrett and Edward Moulton-Barrett live?
9. In which medical soap did Sue Johnston play an hospital adminstrator called Ruth Parry?
10. In *EastEnders*, which character has enjoyed romantic liaisons with Nicki di Marco, Sonia Jackson and Alison Peters?

ANSWERS

1. Bobby Ewing 2. Green 3. *Juliet Bravo* 4. *Children's Ward* 5. Cornwall 6. John Thaw 7. Derek Thompson 8. Wimpole Street (*The Barretts of Wimpole Street*) 9. *Medics* 10. Martin Fowler

QUIZ 213

1 Name either of the US soaps that featured the character of Jake Hanson.

2 Against which profession is the series *The Knock* set?

3 Which actor played a fireman called George Green in *London's Burning*?

4 Which 1990s soap told the story of the relationship between the Thompsons in England and the Stevens in Australia?

5 In *Emmerdale*, Ross Kemp played the illegitimate son of which character?

6 Which *Coronation Street* star wrote the book *The Importance Of Being Percy*?

7 Which member of the Corkhills was played by Sue Jenkins in *Brookside*?

8 Which series featured characters nicknamed Zammo, Pogo, Tegs and Tucker?

9 In which British soap does Matt Milburn play the character of Joe Spencer?

10 What surname connects David, Janet, Ken, Valerie, Tracy, Irma, Ida, Frank and Deirdre?

ANSWERS

1. *Beverly Hills 90210* or *Melrose Place* 2. Customs and excise 3. Glen Murphy 4. *Families* 5. Dolly Skilbeck 6. Bill Waddington 7. Jackie 8. *Grange Hill* 9. *Hollyoaks* 10. Barlow

QUIZ 214

1 What was the occupation of Curly when he first appeared in *Coronation Street*?

2 Which actor plays the role of Curly?

3 What is Curly's real first name?

4 Whom did Curly marry in 2000?

5 Which fashion designer lodged with Curly at No 7 Coronation Street in the 1990s?

6 Whom did Curly buy No 7 Coronation Street from?

7 Which Bettabuys shop assistant was twice engaged to Curly Watts?

8 Curly spent £3000 converting his loft into a what?

9 On which liner did Curly and his first wife Raquel spend their honeymoon?

10 What was Curly nicknamed at school, due to his head being shaped like a light bulb?

ANSWERS

1. Dustbin man 2. Kevin Kennedy 3. Norman 4. Emma Taylor 5. Angie Freeman 6. Rita Fairclough 7. Kimberley Taylor 8. Observatory 9. *QE2* 10. Forty Watts

QUIZ 215

1 Who played the *Coronation Street* character of Jenny Bradley?

2 In which series did Robson Green play a retired soccer star called Michael Flynn?

3 What was the first name of PC Quinnan in *The Bill?*

4 What was the first name of Ricky Butcher's mother in *EastEnders*?

5 In *Dallas*, who accidently set fire to the South Fork ranch in 1983?

6 In which soap do the characters attend St Stephen's Church?

7 In which series does Joe Absolom play a footman called George Cosmo?

8 In which mini-series did David Schwimmer play Lieutenant Sobel of Easy Company?

9 Which series stars Pauline Quirke as the mother of Jake, Lily and Ty?

10 Which medical soap featured a ward sister called Kath Shaughnessy?

ANSWERS

1. Sally Ann Matthews 2. *Rhinoceros* 3. Dave 4. June 5. Ray Krebbs 6. *The Archers* 7. *Servants* 8. *Band Of Brothers* 9. *Being April* 10. *Holby City*

QUIZ 216

1. Which nationality is the Poulos family in *Home And Away*?
2. Which soap actor's career was chronicled in the TV documentary *Ken And Me*?
3. Which star of *Brookside* also played the role of DCI Wise in *Cracker*?
4. Which former star of the sitcom *Hi-De-Hi* went on to play a health care assistant called Stan Hill in *Holby City*?
5. What do the initials CSU stand for with regard to the CSU department in *The Bill*?
6. Who played the role of Roger Huntingdon in *Brookside*?
7. In whcih soap town is the Turpin Road War Memorial?
8. Which character is portrayed by Paula Tilbrook in *Emmerdale*?
9. Which knighted actor played Sir Joseph Channing in *Judge John Deed*?
10. Which seafarer was played by John Woodvine in *Elizabeth R*?

ANSWERS

1. Greek 2. William Roache 3. Ricky Tomlinson 4. Paul Shane 5. Community Safety Unit 6. Rob Spendlove 7. Walford 8. Betty Eagleton 9. Sir Donald Sinden 10. Sir Francis Drake

QUIZ 217

1 In *Brookside,* which member of the Grant clan gave birth to a baby girl called Claire in 1985?

2 What was the name of Barry Grant's drug-addicted girlfriend?

3 Paul Usher, who plays Barry Grant, went on to play which PC in *The Bill*?

4 What was Damon Grant training to be on a YTS course?

5 What was the name of the son Barry Grant fathered with Fran Pearson?

6 What was the name of the engineering firm where Bobby Grant worked until its closure?

7 Who played the role of Karen Grant?

8 In which city did Karen Grant attend university?

9 Which character became the second wife of Bobby Grant?

10 Who accused Barry Grant of murder at a Silver Wedding anniversary party?

ANSWERS

1. Sheila Grant 2. Jane Smith 3. PC Des Taviner 4. Painter and decorator 5. Stephen 6. Fairbanks Engineering 7. Shelagh O'Hara 8. London 9. Susan Morgan 10. Marie Jackson

QUIZ 218

1. Which star of *EastEnders* made her film debut as a schoolgirl in *The Belles Of St Trinians*?
2. Which Weatherfield youngster has been played by Helen Flanagan and Emma Woodward?
3. Which first name has been shared by a Mitchell in *EastEnders*, a Corkhill in *Brookside* and a Walker in *Coronation Street*?
4. What is the name of the George Street Indian restaurant in *EastEnders*?
5. Who played the role of Guthrie Featherstone in *Rumpole Of The Bailey* after previously starring in *To The Manor Born*?
6. Which *Baywatch* star also acted as an executive producer of the show?
7. In which soap did the character of Andrea Zuckerman live in San Fernando Valley?
8. What was the original title of *The Colbys*?
9. Which of the Carrington family was played by Jessica Player?
10. Was *Dr Kildare* first seen by the public as a TV show or a film?

ANSWERS

1. Barbara Windsor 2. Rosie Webster 3. Billy 4. The Argee Bhajee 5. Peter Bowles 6. David Hasselhoff 7. *Beverly Hills 90210* 8. *Dynasty II: The Colbys* 9. Krystina Carrington 10. Film

QUIZ 219

1. Who has played the role of Harry Harper in *Casualty* and *Holby City*?
2. Was Anita Dobson born in 1949, 1950 or 1951?
3. In *Grange Hill,* what was the real first name of Tucker Jenkins?
4. Whose farewell party was held in the Rovers Return at Christmas 1987?
5. Which family moved to 23, Albert Square in 2000?
6. Who played a Bond girl in *Never Say Never Again*, before joining the cast of *Dallas* as Angelica Nero?
7. What is the name of the Bridge Street convenience store in *EastEnders*?
8. In which soap did the character of Kimberley Shaw run a car over her lover Michael Mancini?
9. What is the name of John Boy's mother in *The Waltons*?
10. Which soap featured the character of Warder Meg Morris?

ANSWERS

1. Simon MacCorkindale 2. 1949 3. Peter 4. Hilda Ogden 5. The Slaters 6. Barbara Carrera 7. The Minute Mart 8. *Melrose Place* 9. Olivia 10. *Prisoner Cell Block H*

QUIZ 220

1 In *Coronation Street*, which bigamist did Emily marry?
2 How is Emily related to Spider Nugent?
3 Was Emily's father called Ernest, Edward or Edgar?
4 Was Emily's mother called Agnes, Amy or Annabelle?
5 In which decade was Emily born?
6 In which year did Emily first appear in the soap?
7 In which year of the 1970s did Emily marry Ernest Bishop?
8 In whose factory was Ernest employed as a wages clerk?
9 On which street did Emily run a linen shop?
10 Why did Emily spend a night up a tree in 1998?

ANSWERS

1. Arnold Swain 2. Auntie and nephew 3. Edward 4. Agnes 5. 1920s 6. 1961 7. 1972 8. Mike Baldwin's 9. Rosamund Street 10. In protest over development plans for the Red Rec

QUIZ 221

1. In which soap did Graham Clark murder Rachel Hughes?
2. What is the name of Sally Webster's sister in *Coronation Street*?
3. Who returned as landlady of the Queen Vic in 2001?
4. Which son of Jason and Sable Colby fell in love with Randall?
5. Brian Hibbard, who played Doug Murray in *Coronation Street*, was formerly a member of which pop group?
6. Which character played by Patrick Harvey in *Neighbours* revealed he could not read?
7. How many times did Sue Ellen marry JR Ewing?
8. Stonebank Farm featured in which soap?
9. In which series did former *Soldier Soldier* star Robson Green play DI Dave Creegan?
10. Who played the role of Nurse Sandy Harper in *Holby City*?

ANSWERS

1.*Emmerdale* 2. Gina 3.Sharon Watts 4. Miles Colby 5. The Flying Pickets 6. Connor O'Neill 7. Twice 8. *Crossroads* 9. *Touching Evil* 10. Laura Sadler

QUIZ 222

1 Which song, later a hit for Angry Anderson, was played at the wedding of Scott and Charlene in *Neighbours*?

2 In which US teen soap does Brittany Daniel play the role of Eve?

3 What nickname was bestowed upon the *Brookside* character of David Crosbie?

4 In *Dallas*, whose portrait hung above the fireplace at the Southfork mansion?

5 Which Greg was played by Stephen Billington in *Coronation Street*?

6 In *Dallas*, what is the name of Pamela Ewing's mother?

7 In *EastEnders*, who met his future wife Ruth at an AIDS hospice?

8 In which soap did Hutch Corrigan run a ranch in Bakers Field?

9 What is the last name of Seth the gamekeeper in *Emmerdale*?

10 *South* was a spin-off of which British soap?

ANSWERS

1. 'Suddenly' 2. *Dawson's Creek* 3. Bing 4. Jock Ewing 5. Greg Kelly 6. Rebecca Wentworth 7. Mark Fowler 8. *The Colbys* 9. Armstrong 10. *Brookside*

QUIZ 223

1 In which year of the 1970s did Deirdre first appear in Weatherfield?

2 Was Deirdre's father called David, Derrick or Donald?

3 Which country did her first husband, Ray, move to in 1978?

4 What was Deirdre's first married name?

5 Is Deirdre's middle name Alison, Adele or Anne?

6 Who gave Deirdre away when she married Ken Barlow in 1981?

7 In which year of the 1990s did Deirdre marry her third husband Samir Rachid?

8 In which year did Samir die?

9 At the age of 19, Deirdre was engaged to which 36-year-old character?

10 Who conned Deirdre into believing he was an airline pilot?

ANSWERS

1. 1972 2. Donald 3. Netherlands 4. Langton 5. Anne 6. Alf Roberts 7. 1994 8. 1995 9. Billy Walker 10. Jon Lindsay

QUIZ 224

1 Which 1970s series featured a rock band called The Little Ladies?

2 Did Fred Elliott make his *Coronation Street* debut in 1993, 1994 or 1995?

3 In *EastEnders*, to whom did Tariq Larousi donate a kidney in 2004?

4 In *Coronation Street,* who was the best man at the 2004 wedding of Steve and Karen McDonald?

5 Who died in *Coronation Street* in 2003 and joined the cast of *Where The Heart Is* in 2004 as Ozias Harding?

6 In *The Six Wives Of Henry VIII*, which wife was played by Annette Crosbie?

7 What is the name of Natalie Horrocks' son in *Coronation Street*?

8 Which soap features an on-off relationship between Jesse McGregor and Leah Patterson?

9 What is the unfortunate marriage connection between Weatherfield's Shelley Unwin and Emily Bishop?

10 The series *The Grand* told of life in a hotel in which British city?

ANSWERS

1. *Rock Follies* 2. 1994 3. Ronnie Ferreira 4. Andy McDonald 5. Brian Capron 6. Catherine of Aragon 7. Tony 8. *Home And Away* 9. Both had bigamous marriages 10. Manchester

QUIZ 225

1. What was the name of Harry Hewitt's daughter in *Coronation Street*?
2. Which mountain-dwelling grandfather was portrayed by Will Geer?
3. Which head of *Grange Hill* was played by Gwyneth Powell?
4. Which Erinsborough High School student is played by Kyal Marsh?
5. In 2004 which cleaner professed her love for *Emmerdale*'s Reverend Thomas?
6. Which former *EastEnders* star was a bridesmaid at Liza Minnelli's fourth marriage?
7. In *The Bill*, which PC went on the run after causing a fire that killed six of his colleagues?
8. Which cat-loving character was played by Robyn Moore in *EastEnders*?
9. Which *Neighbours* character sported black hair with blue streaks in 2003?
10. Which *Emmerdale* character was the first lesbian character to appear in a British soap?

ANSWERS

1. Lucille 2. Zeb Walton 3. Bridget McCluskey 4. Boyd Hoyland 5. Laurel Potts 6. Martine McCutcheon 7. PC Des Taviner 8. Shirley Benson 9. Sky Mangel 10. Zoe Tate

QUIZ 226

1. What was the favourite drink of *Coronation Street*'s Ena Sharples in the Rovers Return?
2. Was Ena's husband called Albert, Alexander or Alfred?
3. Did Ena have a daughter called Veronica, Vera or Victoria?
4. Was Ena's son called Ian, Ivan or Isaac?
5. Was Ena's maiden name Spencer, Smith or Schofield?
6. Which number of Coronation Street did Ena inherit in the 1960s?
7. Who played the character of Ena Sharples?
8. In which mission hall did Ena work as a caretaker?
9. What caused Ena to be trapped under the viaduct in 1967?
10. Whose autobiography is entitled *I Was Ena Sharples' Father*?

ANSWERS

1. Milk stout 2. Alfred 3. Vera 4. Ian 5. Schofield 6. Number 11 7. Violet Carson 8. Glad Tidings Mission 9. A train crash 10. Tony Warren

QUIZ 227

1 Which vegetarian PC was played by Kim Tiddy in *The Bill*?

2 Which character was nicknamed "half pint" in *The Little House On The Prairie*?

3 Which Victor was played by Christopher Coll in *Coronation Street*?

4 Which member of the Sugden family is played by Kelvin Fletcher in *Emmerdale*?

5 In *Coronation Street*, what is the job of Karl Foster (played by Chris Finch)?

6 Which series featured the characters of PC Weir, WPC Bayliss and DS Stone?

7 Which soap character played by Bernard Latham ran for the post of Mayor of Hollyoaks?

8 Sam Culver was the first husband of which character in *Dallas*?

9 In *Footballers' Wives*, for which football team did Conrad Gates sign in 2004?

10 In *Emmerdale*, what is the first name of Alan Turner's daughter?

ANSWERS

1. Honey Harman 2. Laura Ingalls 3. Victor Pendlebury 4. Andy Sugden 5. Nurse 6. *Z Cars* 7. Gordon Cunningham 8. Donna Krebbs 9. Earls Park FC 10. Steph

QUIZ 228

•••••••••••••••••••••••••••••

1 In *EastEnders*, who is the older brother: Grant or Phil Mitchell?

2 In which soap was Cassandra Morrell rescued from a Venezuelan prison by a group of mercenaries?

3 What was the first name of PC Garfield in *The Bill*?

4 What is the name of Albert Square's bed and breakfast guest house?

5 In which year was Bethany Platt born in *Coronation Street*?

6 Which Walford family moved into 55 Victoria Road in 2003?

7 Which first name has been shared by a Wicks in *EastEnders*, a Sugden in *Emmerdale* and a Scully in *Neighbours*?

8 Which Katie is played by Sammy Winward in *Emmerdale*?

9 What was the name of the son born to Gary and Judy Mallett in 1998?

10 In *Home And Away*, who was nicknamed Flathead by his pupils?

ANSWERS

1. Phil 2. *Dynasty* 3. George 4. Abercorn B & B 5. 2000 6. The Ferreira family 7. Joe 8. Katie Addyman 9. William 10. Donald Fisher

QUIZ 229

1. In *EastEnders*, who plays the role of Ian Beale?
2. What is the name of Kathy Beale's daughter, whom she gave up for adoption as a teenager?
3. Who is the mother of Ian Beale's twins Peter and Lucy?
4. Who spent three years in prison for the rape of Kathy Beale?
5. What was the name of Lou Beale's husband?
6. Why did Ian Beale separate from his wife Laura, after she announced her pregnancy?
7. How is Pete Beale related to Pauline Fowler?
8. Which member of the Beale family was played by Edward Savage?
9. Is Lou Beale's middle name Agnes, Ada or Agatha?
10. Did Pete Beale usually greet people with the word sugar, honey or treacle?

ANSWERS

1. Adam Woodyatt 2. Donna 3. Cindy Beale (nee Williams) 4. James Wilmott-Brown 5. Albert 6. Ian had undergone a secret vasectomy operation 7. Brother and sister 8. Steven Beale 9. Ada 10. Treacle

QUIZ 230

1. Which ex-wife of Sean Bean played the role of Rita Dolen in *Playing The Field*?
2. Which star of the sitcom *On The Buses* played the role of Alice Pickens in *Coronation Street*?
3. The Grey Gables Hotel features in which soap?
4. In *Coronation Street*, whose children did the 'nanny from hell' Carmel Finnan look after?
5. Which *Emmerdale* character had a short-lived marriage to Christine Sharp?
6. Which soap saw the cast enjoying a drink at the Oil Barons Club?
7. In which New Zealand city is the soap *Shortland Street* set?
8. Which brewery director was played by George Baker in *Coronation Street*?
9. In which British soap did Denise cheat on her husband Les with Caleb?
10. Was Letitia Dean born in 1967, 1968 or 1969?

ANSWERS

1. Melanie Hill 2. Doris Hare 3. *The Archers* 4. Martin and Gail Platt 5. Joe Sugden 6. *Dallas* 7. Auckland 8. Cecil Newton 9. *Family Affairs* 10. 1967

QUIZ 231

• •

1. Which US soap features a company called D and D Advertising?
2. Which couple owned Westfork Ranch in *Knot's Landing*?
3. What type of business is the Arches in *EastEnders*?
4. What is the name of Nick Tilsley's half brother in *Coronation Street*?
5. What is the title of the USA's most popular daytime soap, that features the lead character of Victor Newman?
6. Which US soap features a radio station called KB Rock Radio?
7. What drink was endorsed in a series of adverts by Leonard Rossiter and *Dynasty* star Joan Collins?
8. *Soul City* is the most popular soap in which country?
9. Which Jake is played by Kevin Sacre in *Hollyoaks*?
10. On whose novels was the series *A Touch Of Frost* based?

ANSWERS

1. *Melrose Place* 2. Gary and Abby Ewing 3. Car repair shop 4. David 5. *The Young And The Restless* 6. *Falcon Crest* 7. Cinzano 8. South Africa 9. Jake Dean 10. RD Wingfield

QUIZ 232

In *Emmerdale* ...

1 Which vet delivered Belle Dingle into the world?
2 Which Dingle married his girlfriend on his hospital death bed?
3 Which member of the Dingle family is played by James Hooton?
4 Which of the Dingles landed a job as a chef at Eric Pollard's wine bar?
5 Which of the Dingles, played by Emma Atkins, was charged with murdering her husband?
6 What is the name of Mandy Dingle's father?
7 What is the name of Zak Dingles elder brother?
8 Which actor plays the role of Cain Dingle?
9 The funeral of which Dingle family member was held in February 2004?
10 What was the name of Butch Dingle's pet rat?

ANSWERS

1. Paddy Kirk 2. Butch Dingle 3. Sam Dingle 4. Marlon Dingle 5. Charity Dingle 6. Caleb 7. Shadrach 8. Jeff Hordley 9. Tricia Dingle 10. Jessica

QUIZ 233

1 Which long-distance lorry driver was played by Jack Watson in *Coronation Street*?

2 Which soap produced a video spin-off entitled *The Lost Weekend*?

3 Sita Sharma, Lynne Harrison and Colette Johnson were all characters in which short-lived soap?

4 Which Sun Hill detective sergeant resigned after punching Inspector Monroe in the face?

5 Which soap has the same title as a 2002 film starring Britney Spears and a 1986 film starring Ralph Macchio?

6 Which season of the year provides the first name of the *Neighbours* character played by Mansa Siketa?

7 What is Gus short for, in the name of *EastEnders* character Gus Smith?

8 In which soap does Mitch Firth play the role of Seb Miller?

9 In *EastEnders*, which member of the Moon family is played by Andrew Paul?

10 Which *Coronation Street* toddler has been played by twins Amy and Emily Walton?

ANSWERS

1. Bill Gregory 2. *Brookside* 3. *Albion Market* 4. Ted Roach 5. *Crossroads* 6. Summer 7. Augustus 8. *Home And Away* 9. Maxwell Moon 10. Bethany Platt

QUIZ 234

1 Who plays the title role in the TV series *Linda Green*?

2 Which soap opera village is situated in the Valley Of The River Am?

3 Which first name is shared by a Woods in *Emmerdale*, a Sullivan in *The Sullivans* and a Duckworth in *Coronation Street*?

4 What is the name of the novelist sister of soap actress Joan Collins?

5 Which soap star was born Patsy Ann McClenny?

6 The former *Coronation Street* star Charles Dale plays the role of Clive Eustace in which TV series?

7 Which Weatherfield newspaper is sold in the Kabin?

8 In which soap did the character of Brooke, played by Kristen Davis, drown in a swimming pool and return as a ghost?

9 What was the nationality of DC Alistair Greig in *The Bill*?

10 Who had a hit record with the song 'Right Said Fred' in 1962 and joined the cast of *Coronation Street* 41 years later?

ANSWERS

1. Liza Tarbuck 2. Ambridge in *The Archers* 3. Terry 4. Jackie Collins 5. Morgan Fairchild 6. *Paradise Heights* 7. Weatherfield Gazette 8. *Melrose Place* 9. Scottish 10. Bernard Cribbins

QUIZ 235

1. Whom did Mike Baldwin marry in 2000?
2. What is Mike's favourite drink in the Rovers?
3. What is the name of Mike's underwear factory?
4. In which city was Mike Baldwin born?
5. Whom did Mike marry in 1991 and divorce in the same year?
6. What was the name of Mike's garage that he purchased and set up at 16 Coronation Street?
7. In which year did Mike marry Alma Sedgewick?
8. What was the name of the first clothes factory that Mike set up in Weatherfield?
9. Did Mike move to Weatherfield in 1975, 1976 or 1977?
10. What is Mike Baldwin's middle name?

ANSWERS

1. Linda Sykes 2. Scotch 3. Underworld 4. London 5. Jackie Ingram 6. MVB Motors 7. 1992 8. Baldwin's Casuals 9. 1976 10. Vernon

QUIZ 236

1. By which acronym is the Soap Opera Digest Awards known?
2. Della Alexander and Binnie Roberts were the first lesbian couple in which soap?
3. In which soap did Jamie, Kristian, Max and Theo find themselves trapped during a potholing trip?
4. Which soap features a pub called The Black Swan?
5. In *EastEnders,* which character has a bench in Albert Square commemorating his memory?
6. During which war was *M.A.S.H.* set?
7. What is the first name of the *Falcon Crest* character whose surnames have included Gioberti, Channing and Stavros?
8. What is the first name of Superintendant Okaro in *The Bill*?
9. In which city is the US soap *The Bold And The Beautiful* set?
10. Which series has screened episodes entitled *The Love Of Johnny Johnson*, *Wilder And Wilder* and *Marvin's Garden*?

ANSWERS

1. SODAs 2. *EastEnders* 3. *Hollyoaks* 4. *Family Affairs* 5. Arthur Fowler 6. Korean War 7. Angela 8. Adam 9. Los Angeles 10. *The Little House On The Prairie*

QUIZ 237

1 In which series did *Coronation Street* star Margi Clarke play a factory worker called Queenie?

2 In which soap did the character of Sidney Gibbs own a cleaning business called Sid's Scrubbers?

3 In *Brookside*, at which Premiership football ground did Sinbad propose to his girlfriend?

4 Who died first in *Coronation Street*, Stan Ogden, Renee Roberts or Len Fairclough?

5 Lee, Rosie, Sarah and Carl were all members of which *Brookside* family?

6 What is the name William Roache's son, who for a time played his son Peter in *Coronation Street*?

7 Which Ewing married Mitch Cooper?

8 Who played the role of Iris McKay in *Beverly Hills 90210*?

9 The Australian soaps *The Young Doctors* and *Sons And Daughters* were both set in which city?

10 Which comedian played the role of Jeff Evans in *Brookside*?

ANSWERS

1. *Making Out* 2. *EastEnders* 3. *Goodison Park* 4. Renee Roberts 5. The Banks family 6. Linus Roache 7. Lucy Ewing 8. Stephanie Beacham 9. Sydney 10. Les Dennis

QUIZ 238

1. Which Walford resident did Den get pregnant when she was only 16?
2. What was the name of the daughter born as a result of the affair?
3. What is the name of Dirty Den's son?
4. Why did Den set fire to the Dagmar Wine Bar?
5. What is the name of the night club that Den runs with his adopted daughter Sharon?
6. What did Den give his wife for Christmas in 1986?
7. In which year did Dirty Den first leave the soap, as a suspected murder victim?
8. Which Jan was the name of Den's long-term upper-class mistress?
9. What was the name of the wine bar that Den managed for a local protection racket?
10. Who plays the role of Dirty Den?

ANSWERS

1. Michelle Fowler 2. Vicki 3. Dennis Rickman 4. In revenge for Wilmott-Brown's assault on Kathy Beale 5. Angie's Den 6. Divorce papers 7. 1989 8. Jan Hammond 9. Strokes Wine Bar 10. Leslie Grantham

QUIZ 239

1. Who plays the role of Kirk Sutherland in *Coronation Street*?
2. Was the last episode of *Falcon Crest* screened in 1988, 1989 or 1990?
3. In *Hollyoaks*, which character is a mobile hairdresser and a cabaret singer?
4. In *EastEnders*, what is the name of Nick Cotton's wife?
5. In *Crossroads*, what is the first name of the character whose surnames have been Richardson, Harvey and Chance?
6. Which member of the Colby clan was played by Kim Morgan Greene?
7. Which character in *Family Affairs* set up a business called Cash And Dash?
8. Who played Hawkeye in the TV series *M.A.S.H.*?
9. What won the 2001 BAFTA for Best Soap?
10. About which programme did *Daily Mirror* journalist Ken Irwin write "The programme is doomed", after it first appeared?

ANSWERS

1. Andrew Whyment 2. 1990 3. Frankie Dean 4. Zoe 5. Jill 6. Channing Colby 7. Pete Callan 8. Alan Alda 9. *Emmerdale* 10. *Coronation Street*

QUIZ 240

1 Which of the McGann brothers played the role of Gary Halliwell in *The Manageress*?

2 In *Emmerdale*, what is written on the side of Zak Dingle's van?

3 In *The Bill*, which sergeant's baby daughter died in February 2004?

4 Which soap follows the lives of the employees of a budget airline called Fresh?

5 *Movin' On* was a late night spin-off of which soap?

6 Which doctor was played by Justin Melvey in *Home And Away*?

7 In *Neighbours*, which member of the Stark family has been played by Todd MacDonald?

8 Which former *Coronation Street* star landed the stage role of Amos Hart in a 2004 West End production of *Chicago*?

9 Which *Brookside* character was often referred to by her initials of DD?

10 In *Coronation Street*, who attempted to sabotage the 2004 wedding of Steve and Karen?

ANSWERS

1. Mark McGann 2. Dingle and Kirk, General Builders 3. Sheelagh Murphy 4. *Mile High* 5. *Hollyoaks* 6. Harry Reynolds 7. Darren Stark 8. Kevin Kennedy 9. Debra Dixon 10. Tracy Barlow

QUIZ 241

1. Whose window-cleaning round did the Duckworths buy in 1984?
2. Who moved into the Duckworths' house as a lodger in 1988?
3. In which street did Jack and Vera Duckworth live in rented accommodation before moving to Coronation Street.
4. What did the Duckworths buy from Eunice Gee?
5. What did the Duckworths buy in 1995 after inheriting £30,000?
6. What is Vera Duckworth's real first name?
7. What is the name of Jack Duckworth's older brother?
8. Is Jack Duckworth's middle name Harold, Howard or Hubert?
9. Was Vera Duckworth's maiden name Burton, Bennett or Bradshaw?
10. Was their only son Terry born in 1963, 1964 or 1965?

ANSWERS

1. Stan Ogdens 2. Curly Watts 3. Inkerman Street 4. A boarding house 5. The Rovers Return 6. Veronica 7. Cliff 8. Howard 9. Burton 10. 1964

QUIZ 242

1. In 1994 which *Emmerdale* character married Shirley Foster?
2. Which soap features a pair of teenage lovers called Harley Lawson and Shannon Donnelly?
3. On whose novel was the soap mini-series *The Man Who Made Husbands Jealous* based?
4. Which member of the Clarke family is played by Angus McLaren in *Neighbours*?
5. Janine, Laura and Lynn all left which soap in 2004?
6. What is the nationality of the *Hollyoaks* character Natalie Osborne?
7. Who has played the roles of Geraldine in *The Grimleys*, Mia in *Cutting It* and Carmen in *EastEnders*?
8. In 2004, which long-serving *Neighbours* character suffered a stroke that resulted in a dramatic change of personality?
9. In *Emmerdale,* what is the job of the character of Carlos Diaz?
10. Who played Sheila Sabatini in Surgical Spirit before joining the cast of *Coronation Street* as Anita Scott?

ANSWERS

1. Alan Turner 2. *Footballers' Wives* 3. Jilly Cooper 4. Jamie 5. *EastEnders* 6. Scottish 7. Amanda Holden 8. Harold Bishop 9. Chef 10. Nichola McAuliffe

QUIZ 243

1. Dr Gail Benson and Dr Robert Nevin are characters in which medical soap?
2. Which *Emmerdale* character died in a shooting accident in August 1989?
3. In *Brookside*, which nightclub was destroyed by an explosion in 1999?
4. In *Neighbours*, what is the unusual first name of Stephen Gottlieb's sister?
5. What did Roy and Hayley Cropper call their baby, which they bought from Tracy Barlow?
6. In *EastEnders*, who professed his love for his adoptive sister Sharon?
7. Which *Emmerdale* character is portrayed by Charlotte Bellamy?
8. Which *Hollyoaks* character, played by Nick Pickard, was engaged to two women at the same time?
9. What is Maya Sharma's job in *Coronation Street*?
10. Which *Neighbours* character was killed on her wedding day in 2003?

ANSWERS

1. *Medics* 2. Jackie Merrick 3. The Millennium Club 4. Serendipity 5. Patience 6. Dennis Rickman 7. Laurel Potts 8. Tony Hutchinson 9. Solicitor 10. Dee Bliss

QUIZ 244

1. At which supermarket did Andy McDonald undergo a management trainee programme?
2. Was Liz McDonald's maiden name Grainger, Greaves or Greenwood?
3. Which Newton and Ridley pub was managed by Liz McDonald?
4. In which year of the 1970s were the McDonald twins Andy and Steve born?
5. What was the name of the t-shirt company established by Steve McDonald?
6. What was the name of Jim and Liz's daughter, who died when she was just one day old?
7. Why was Steve McDonald sentenced to two years in prison?
8. Which girlfriend of Andy McDonald had a son called Dominic?
9. Which European country did Vicki McDonald move to when she split from Steve?
10. Where did Steve marry Karen for the first time in 2001?

ANSWERS

1. Bettabuys 2. Greenwood 3. The Queens 4. 1974 5. Dun 2 AT 6. Katie 7. Perverting the course of justice 8. Amy Nelson 9. Switzerland 10. Weatherfield Registry Office

QUIZ 245

1. Whose 80th birthday party was held in the Queen Vic in Februrary 1996?
2. In *Neighbours,* was Hannah Martin's horse called Pointer, Prancer or Painter?
3. The Fairlawns Hotel was a rival of which business?
4. In *Home And Away,* Rhys Sutherland is a former professional star of which sport?
5. How did Dot Cotton's first husband die?
6. In which country did Nick Tilsley marry Leanne Battersby?
7. Which Weatherfield youngster is played by Sam Ashton?
8. In which US series did Michael Tucker play Stuart Markowitz?
9. In *EastEnders,* who stood trial for the attempted murder of Phil Mitchell?
10. Who landed the role of Lauren Harris in *Fat Friends* after dying in Weatherfield?

ANSWERS

1. Ethel Skinner 2. Painter 3. Crossroads Motel 4. Australian Rules Football 5. In a lorry crash 6. Scotland 7. Chesney Brown 8. *LA Law* 9. Dan Sullivan 10. Gaynor Faye

QUIZ 246

1. Which member of the Taylor family is played by Brooke Kinsella in *EastEnders*?
2. Which DC is played by Diane Parish in *The Bill*?
3. What is the name of the young bride of Terry Woods in *Emmerdale*?
4. Which *Dynasty* character suffered brain damage after falling from a horse?
5. In which soap do people live in the Summer Bay Caravan Park?
6. Potter, Tilsley, Platt: which surname comes next?
7. In *Emmerdale*, who gave birth to twins called Sam and Sally?
8. Kitty, Brian and Dick were all members of which *Crossroads* family?
9. In *Coronation Street* who has professed his love for Maureen, Veronica and Yvonne?
10. Which role has been played on film by John Alderton and on TV by Christopher Timothy?

ANSWERS

1. Kelly Taylor 2. Eva Sharpe 3. Dawn 4. Krystal Carrington 5. *Home And Away* 6. Hillman (Gail's surnames in *Coronation Street)* 7. Dolly Skilbeck 8. Jarvis 9. Reg Holdsworth 10. James Herriot

QUIZ 247

In *Coronation Street* . . .

1 What was the name of Bet's boyfriend with whom she rented a flat in Victoria Street?

2 How was Bet's son Martin killed in 1975?

3 Which married man did Bet have an affair with in 1982?

4 Is Bet's middle name Theresa, Tina or Tracy?

5 Whose marriage proposal did Bet accept in 1987?

6 In 1994 which lorry driver left Bet for the Rovers barmaid Tanya Pooley?

7 In what year of the 1960s did Bet first appear in *Coronation Street*?

8 Who plays the role of Bet Lynch?

9 Which policeman did Bet have an affair with in 1984?

10 Did Bet first work at the Rovers Return in 1969, 1970 or 1971?

ANSWERS

1. Frank Bradley 2. Car crash 3. Jack Duckworth 4. Theresa 5. Alec Gilroy 6. Charlie Wheelan 7. 1966 8. Julie Goodyear 9. Tony Cunliffe 10. 1970

QUIZ 248

1 Who bought Gary Ewing's Knot's Landing home as a gift?

2 By what two letters is the character played by Daniel Anthony in *EastEnders* known?

3 Who played the role of Hector MacDonald in *Monarch Of The Glen*?

4 In May 1977 which *Emmerdale* character married a young bride called Dee De La Cruz?

5 Which series featured a drill foreman called Nick Kimball?

6 In which soap did Cameron, Lee, Bombhead and Norman form a band called The X Factor?

7 Which actress plays the matron in the *Heartbeat* spin off *The Royal*?

8 Which soap features an eccentric gossip called Colleen Smart?

9 Who plays the role of Terry Woods in *Emmerdale*?

10 Who died first in *Coronation Street*: Jez Quigley, Alison Webster or Duggie Ferguson?

ANSWERS

1. Miss Ellie Ewing 2. JJ 3. Richard Briers 4. Eric Pollard 5. *Dynasty* 6. *Hollyoaks* 7. Wendy Craig 8. *Home And Away* 9. Billy Hartman 10. Alison Webster

QUIZ 249

1. Which *Neighbours* character owns his own construction company?
2. In which series did *EastEnders* star Leslie Grantham play the role of Mick Raynor?
3. What kind of animal killed the *Emmerdale* character of Dennis Rigg?
4. What is the occupation of Curly Watts' second wife Emma?
5. Which PE teacher at Grange Hill was nicknamed Bullet?
6. Which police constable married a nurse called Jenny Delaney in *The Bill*?
7. Which *EastEnders* couple fostered Jessie Moore?
8. In *Brookside*, who killed Clint Moffat?
9. What was the first name of PC McGann in *The Bill*?
10. Which Walford social worker is played by Chizzy Akudolu?

ANSWERS

1. Joe Scully 2. *99-1* 3. A bull crushed him to death 4. Police sergeant 5. Mr Baxter 6. PC Quinnan 7. Mark and Ruth Fowler 8. Ron Dixon 9. Gary 10. Mattie George

QUIZ 250

1. In *Dynasty,* Alexis received a prison sentence for whose murder?
2. Who suffered a fatal heart attack while having sex with Alexis?
3. Which character had a fight with Alexis in a lily pond?
4. Who attempted to kill Alexis by gassing her?
5. With which king did Alexis have an affair?
6. With which congressman did Alexis have an affair?
7. Which cowboy did Alexis fall madly in love with?
8. What was the name of Amanda Carrington's boyfriend, whom Alexis had an affair with?
9. In 1988, did Sean Rowan have an affair with Alexis, shoot her or steal her jewellery?
10. In which year did Alexis first appear in *Dynasty*?

ANSWERS

1. Mark Jennings 2. Cecil Colby 3. Krystle Carrington 4. Jeremy Van Dorm 5. King Galen 6. Neal McVane 7. Dex Dexter 8. Michael Culhane 9. Shot her 10. 1981

QUIZ 251

1. In which series does Leslie Ash play Inspector Charlie Eden?
2. In *Dynasty*, what was the nationality of the millionaire Peter de Vilbis?
3. Which soap features a used-car business called Deals On Wheels?
4. Which *Coronation Street* regular plays the role of Flo Henshaw in *Two Pints Of Lager And A Packet Of Crisps*?
5. Which convicted killer did Paul Robinson marry in *Neighbours*?
6. Which *Emmerdale* couple have lived in Hawthorn Cottage and Woodside Farm?
7. In which fictional town is *A Touch Of Frost* set?
8. Which *EastEnders* character died in 1996, from head injuries sustained in a prison riot?
9. In November 1996 which *Emmerdale* character married Dave Glover?
10. Which *Summer Bay* heart throb is played by Nic Testoni?

ANSWERS

1. *Merseybeat* 2. Brazilian 3. *EastEnders* 4. Beverley Callard 5. Terri Inglis 6. Jack and Sarah Sugden 7. Denton 8. Arthur Fowler 9. Kathy Tate 10. Travis Nash

QUIZ 252

1 Which character returned to Albert Square in 2000, running a business called Romantic Relations?

2 Who joined the cast of *Coronation Street* in 2004 playing the nephew of Mike Baldwin?

3 In *EastEnders,* which nurse was engaged to Jamie Mitchell at the time of his death?

4 In *Coronation Street,* is Fred Elliott's middle name Handel, Beethoven or Amadeus?

5 In *EastEnders*, in which street is the market located?

6 In *Coronation Street,* who gave birth to a baby daughter on Christmas Eve 1990?

7 What is Ash Ferreria's job in *EastEnders*?

8 Which *Coronation Street* character has had the surnames of Naylor, Holdsworth and Elliott?

9 Who plays the mother of Simon and David Wicks in *EastEnders*?

10 Which *Coronation Street* character had an affair with a nursing work colleague called Cathy Power?

ANSWERS

1. Natalie Evans 2. Bradley Walsh 3. Sonia Jackson 4. Handel 5. Bridge Street 6. Sally Webster 7. College lecturer 8. Maureen 9. Pam St Clement 10. Martin Platt

QUIZ 253

1. Which free newspaper was edited by Ken Barlow?
2. Who played Ken Barlow's posh girlfriend Elaine Perkins?
3. What was the name of Ken Barlow's father?
4. Against which newspaper did William Roache win a libel case, after it had labelled him as boring?
5. What was the maiden name of Ken's first wife?
6. Whom did Susan Barlow marry, much to the chagrain of Ken?
7. What was the first name of Ken's second wife?
8. On which Greek island did Ken honeymoon with his third wife Deirdre?
9. In which year of the 1980s did Ken's Uncle Albert die?
10. Why did Ken spend seven days in a prison cell in 1967?

ANSWERS

1. *Weatherfield Recorder* 2. Joanna Lumley 3. Frank 4. *The Sun* 5. Valerie Tatlock 6. Mike Baldwin 7. Janet 8. Corfu 9. 1984 10. He was arrested on a protest march against the Vietnam War

QUIZ 254

1. Which *Emmerdale* character married Linda Glover on Christmas Eve 1996?
2. In which soap did a freak earthquake hit a caravan park in 2004?
3. What name has been shared by an Owen in *Albion Market*, a Wilton in Weatherfield and a Harkinson in Walford?
4. In *Footballers' Wives* what is the name of the club chairman played by John Forgeham?
5. What was the title of the *Emmerdale* spin-off that chronicled the honeymoon of Mandy Dingle in Venice?
6. In which country did *Coronation Street* character Ivy Brennan die?
7. Which *Coronation Street* actress was portrayed by Denise Black in the TV drama *The Things You Do For Love*?
8. Which surname is shared by Scott and Dawn in *Emmerdale*?
9. In *Knot's Landing*, which character had the surnames of Cunningham, Ewing and Sumner?
10. Which *Neighbours* teenager is played by Lara Sacher?

ANSWERS

1. Biff Fowler 2. *Home And Away* 3. Derek 4. Frank Laslett 5. *Don't Look Now - The Dingles In Venice* 6. Ireland 7. Pat Phoenix 8. Windsor 9. Abby 10. Serena Bishop

QUIZ 255

1. Which *EastEnders* actor recorded an album entitled *Once Around The Sun*?
2. In *Neighbours* which character posed nude for a magazine called *Ambrosia*?
3. In which year of the 1980s was the last episode of *The Sullivans* broadcast?
4. What is the job of *Hollyoaks* character Ben Davies?
5. In which soap did Dr Goodwin woo student nurse Samantha Beaumont on a surfing trip?
6. In *Coronation Street* is Tyrone Dobbs' middle name Simon, Sebastian or Sylvester?
7. Which former *Hollyoaks* star joined the cast of *Casualty* as a psychiatric nurse called Abs?
8. What was the name of the house that Frank Tate bought Chris and Kathy Tate for a wedding present in *Emmerdale*?
9. Who is the real-life famous father of *EastEnders* star Hannah Waterman?
10. Which *Coronation Street* character faced emergency surgery in April 2003 after being shot in a revenge attack?

ANSWERS

1. Shane Richie 2. Lucy Robinson 3. 1982 4. Fireman 5. *The Royal* 6. Sylvester 7. James Redmond 8. The Mills 9. Dennis Waterman 10. Tommy Nelson

QUIZ 256

1. Why did Grant Mitchell beat up Queen Vic landlord Eddie Royle?
2. Whom did Jamie Mitchell lose his virginity to?
3. What is the name of the Mitchell brothers' crooked solicitor, played by Stephen Churchett?
4. Which South American country did Grant Mitchell flee to with his daughter Courtney?
5. What is the name of Grant and Phil's sister?
6. What was the name of the Mitchell brothers' father?
7. Did Grant marry Sharon Watts on April Fools Day, St George's Day or Boxing Day?
8. How is Billy Mitchell related to Phil and Grant?
9. What is the name of Tiffany Mitchell's mother, who slept with Grant?
10. What was the name of Phil and Kathy Mitchell's nanny played by Tara Lynne O'Neill?

ANSWERS

1. For making a pass at his wife Sharon 2. Janine Butcher 3. Marcus Christie 4. Brazil 5. Sam 6. Eric 7. Boxing Day 8. Second cousin 9. Louise 10. Joanne Ryan

QUIZ 257

1 *Movin' On* was a late-night spin-off of which soap?
2 Where on *Coronation Street* did Mike Baldwin share a flat with Bet Lynch?
3 In which year of the 1960s did *Dr Kildare* make its TV debut?
4 In *Footballers' Wives*, what is the job of Elaine Hardy at Earls Park FC?
5 In *Coronation Street,* which character died first: Alma Baldwin, Des Barnes or Judy Mallett?
6 In *EastEnders*, how many years was Little Mo sentenced to for attempted murder?
7 In which country was the soap mini-series *The Thorn Birds* set?
8 Carol Hanley is the natural mother of which *EastEnders* character?
9 What colour did Vera Duckworth's hair turn after a trip to the hairdressers in 2003?
10 What was Steve Elliot's job in the Queen Vic?

ANSWERS

1. *Hollyoaks* 2. Over the corner shop 3. 1961 4. Physiotherapist 5. Des Barnes 6. Eight years 7. Australia 8. Sharon Watts 9. Purple 10. Chef

QUIZ 258

1. In *EastEnders*, which business has the address of The Arches, 2 Turpin Way?
2. Which *Home And Away* character played by Rowena Wallace was diagnosed with kleptomania?
3. What was Melanie Owen's maiden name before her marriage to Walford villain Steve Owen?
4. In *Coronation Street*, what is the name of Dev Alahan's father?
5. In *Hollyoaks*, who left Tony Hutchinson standing at the altar in 2002?
6. Which soap was axed by ITV bosses in 2003, only months after its relaunch?
7. In *Coronation Street*, is Terry Duckworth's middle name Edgar, Ernest or Eric?
8. Which series set in Newcastle chronicled 30 years in the lives of four friends called Nicky, Geordie, Tosker and Mary?
9. Which star of *EastEnders* also played Mrs Hill in *Thomas And Sarah* and Mrs Eckersley in *Emmerdale Farm*?
10. In which soap does Carol Boyd play Linda Snell?

ANSWERS

1. Mitchells Autos 2. June Reynolds 3. Healy 4. Ranjiv 5. Julie Matthews 6. *Crossroads* 7. Edgar 8. *Our Friends In The North* 9. Pam St Clement 10. *The Archers*

QUIZ 259

In *Coronation Street* . . .

1. In which year of the 1980s did Stan Ogden die?
2. What was Hilda Ogden's maiden name?
3. Which type of birds decorated the living-room wall of the Ogdens?
4. Jean Alexander, who played Hilda, also played the mother of which prostitute in the film *Scandal*?
5. Who played the role of Stan Ogden?
6. What is the name of Hilda and Stan's son?
7. Who became Hilda Ogden's lodger in 1985?
8. What did Hilda Ogden usually wear in her hair?
9. Which wedding anniversary did the Ogden's celebrate in 1983?
10. Which mountain range adorned the mural on the Ogden's living-room wall?

ANSWERS

1. 1984 2. Crabtree 3. Flying ducks 4. Christine Keeler 5. Bernard Youens 6. Trevor 7. Kevin Webster 8. Curlers 9. Ruby (40 years) 10. Swiss Alps

QUIZ 260

1. In *EastEnders,* who died first: Roy Evans, Steve Owen or Barry Evans?
2. At which college did the soap character Darlene Taylor begin an A Level course?
3. In which US soap did Karen Allen play Annie Fairgate?
4. In which city was the series *Queer As Folk* set?
5. Which oil company was Wilson Crider head of in *Dallas*?
6. In *EastEnders*, what was the name of the dog that Janine Butcher received for an 18th birthday present?
7. Which soap featured a business called Carpenter's Mechanics?
8. Which country did Lucy Ewing move to when she left Southfork in 1990?
9. Which character went missing in *Neighbours* for five years, returning in the guise of 'Ted'?
10. Which series has had episodes entitled *The Return Of Jessie*, *Lines In The Sand* and *Dolphin Quest*?

ANSWERS

1. Steve Owen 2. Hollyoaks Community College 3. *Knot's Landing* 4. Manchester 5. Weststar Oil 6. Terrence 7. *Neighbours* 8. Italy 9. Harold Bishop 10. *Baywatch*

QUIZ 261

1 Which star of *Dallas* penned an autobiography entitled *Hello Darlin'*?

2 Did Reg Holdsworth first appear in *Coronation Street* in 1987, 1988 or 1989?

3 What type of sports car did PC Nick Ramsay drive in *The Bill*?

4 Who lived in a house called Inglebrook before moving into the Woolpack?

5 In *Dallas*, which character was a former winner of the Miss Texas Beauty Pageant?

6 Who plays the role of Donald Fisher in *Home And Away*?

7 What crime was Ron Dixon charged with in 2001?

8 What was the name of Jenna Wade and Bobby Ewing's son?

9 What was the first name of DS Daly in *The Bill*?

10 Which of *The Three Musketeers* did Jim Bob Walton name his pet guinea pig after?

ANSWERS

1. Larry Hagman 2. 1989 3. Porsche 4. Henry Wilks 5. Sue Ellen Ewing 6. Norman Coburn 7. Murder 8. Lucas 9. Geoff 10. Porthos

QUIZ 262

1. At which number of Albert Square do the Fowlers live?
2. Ruth Fowler left her husband Mark to live in Scotland with which character?
3. Which trade union steward's proposal of marriage was turned down by Pauline Fowler?
4. Which wife of Mark Fowler died of AIDS?
5. What relation is Pauline Fowler to Mary Flaherty?
6. Who was the father of Michelle Fowler's son Mark?
7. Whom did Arthur Fowler have an affair with, while working as her gardener?
8. Which daughter of Martin Fowler was given up for adoption?
9. Who played the role of Ruth Fowler?
10. Who framed Arthur Fowler for embezzlement, which resulted in a second spell in prison?

ANSWERS

1. 45 2. Conor Flaherty 3. Jeff Healy 4. Jill 5. Aunt 6. Grant Mitchell 7. Christine Hewitt 8. Chloe 9. Caroline Paterson 10. Willy Roper

QUIZ 263

1. What is the name of the Scully's dog in *Neighbours*?
2. In *Coronation Street*, what religion did Ivy Brennan adhere to?
3. In *EastEnders*, who was framed for the murder of Saskia Duncan?
4. In 1997, which US soap actor was elected Vice President of the National Rifle Association?
5. Which soap family employed a law firm called Smithfield and Bennet?
6. Which *Emmerdale* character has had the surnames of Wylie, Dingle and Kirk?
7. How did Snowball Merryman commit suicide in *Bad Girls*?
8. In 2002, which star of *EastEnders* penned an autobiography entitled *All Of Me*?
9. In which city was *Shoestring* set?
10. In 1988 Nicholas Peace fell to his death from a balcony after a struggle with which soap villain?

ANSWERS

1. Harvey 2. Roman Catholic 3. Matthew Rose 4. Charlton Heston 5. *The Ewings* 6. Emily 7. Hung herself 8. Barbara Windsor 9. Bristol 10. JR Ewing

QUIZ 264

1 Who played Nick in *Holby City*, Tom in *Born And Bred* and David in *EastEnders*?

2 Who played the roles of Debbie Bates in *EastEnders* and Cat Webb in *Family Affairs*?

3 Who was voted Top Soap Villain of all time in a 2003 TV Times poll?

4 What is the first name of DS Hunter in *The Bill*?

5 In *EastEnders*, who got Kat Slater pregnant when she was 13 years old?

6 In *Coronation Street*, which crooked cop framed Les Battersby for assault?

7 In 2003, which star of *EastEnders* cycled from Lands End to John O'Groats to raise funds for Cancer Research?

8 In which area of London was the medical soap *Angels* set?

9 Which actor, who played the role of Mike Wilson in *London's Burning*, died in 2002?

10 In the *EastEnders* episode entitled *The Return Of Nick Cotton*, who appeared to Nick as a ghost?

ANSWERS

1. Michael French 2. Nicola Duffett 3. Richard Hillman 4. Phil 5. Her uncle, Harry Slater 6. Mick Hopwood 7. Adam Woodyatt 8. Battersea 9. James Hazeldine 10. His father, Charlie Cotton

QUIZ 265

1. What is the name of Elsie Tanner's son?
2. Whom did Elsie marry in 1970?
3. What is the name of Elsie's daughter?
4. Which *Coronation Street* regular twice proposed to Elsie, being turned down on each occasion?
5. Was the name of Elsie's first husband: Arnold, Albert or Amos?
6. Was Elsie's sister called Fiona, Fay or Florence?
7. What was the nationality of Elsie's second husband Steve?
8. Which actor played her second husband, Steve?
9. Which star of *Till Death Us Do Part* married Pat Phoenix in real life?
10. In which year did Elsie Tanner leave Weatherfield for a new life in Portugal?

ANSWERS

1. Dennis 2. Alan Howard 3. Linda 4. Len Fairclough 5. Arnold 6. Fay 7. American 8. Paul Maxwell 9. Anthony Booth 10. 1984

QUIZ 266

1 In *EastEnders*, who was the godfather of Jamie Mitchell?

2 Which gay sergeant replaced Sergeant Bob Cryer in *The Bill*?

3 In *Emmerdale* was Vic Windsor killed in a pub, a post office or a barn?

4 Was the soap actor Johnny Briggs born in 1935, 1936 or 1937?

5 In *Falcon Crest*, which surname links the characters of Julia, Lance and Tony?

6 Who was the co-creator of *EastEnders* with Julia Smith?

7 Which character in *Hollyoaks* is a diabetic?

8 Which member of the Fowler clan returned to Albert Square from the USA in 2003?

9 Which *Coronation Street* actor once performed in a pop group called The Paris Valentinoes?

10 Weatherfield romeo Dev Alahan has shared a bed with which mother and daughter in *Coronation Street*?

ANSWERS

1. Phil Mitchell 2. Sergeant Craig Gilmore 3. Post office 4. 1935 5. Cumson 6. Tony Holland 7. Dan Hunter 8. Vicki Fowler 9. Kevin Kennedy 10. Tracy Barlow and her mother Deirdre

QUIZ 267

1. Little Mo Slater was found guilty of the attempted murder of whom?
2. Which pop star made a guest appearance as himself in a *Hollyoaks* 2002 New Years Eve party?
3. Which *Neighbours* star topped the Australian charts in 2002 with the song 'Born To Try'?
4. Which *EastEnders* character became the manager of Steve Owen's nightclub after losing his job as a vice cop?
5. In *Coronation Street*, was Janice Battersby's maiden name Lawson, Lee or Leighton?
6. Which soap featured a newspaper called the *Denver Mirror*?
7. How were the *Street* characters of Alma Baldwin and Richard Hillman related?
8. What was the name of Rita Sullivan's pet shih-tzu?
9. Which former *Neighbours* star played an Australian backpacker called Jules Robinson in *Coronation Street*?
10. How was *Casualty* nurse Jude Kocarnik killed?

ANSWERS

1. Trevor Morgan 2. Boy George 3. Delta Goodrem 4. Beppe di Marco 5. Lee 6. *Dynasty* 7. Cousins 8. Mr Woo 9. Rebecca Ritters 10. Stabbed

QUIZ 268

1. What was the name of the rebellious punk rocker played by Linda Davidson in *EastEnders*?
2. Which former *Eastender* starred as Natalie in the 2003 film *Love Actually*?
3. Who played the Walford villain Trevor Morgan?
4. Dan, Kareena and Ronny share which surname in *EastEnders*?
5. Which homeland country did Tony Carpenter return to when he left Walford?
6. What object did Steve Owen use to strike the fatal blow that killed his girlfriend Saskia?
7. Which Walford character lost his taxi licence in 2004?
8. Which Walford character was played by Ricky Groves?
9. Which East End market trader was the father of David Wicks?
10. In 2004, who confessed to killing Barry Evans?

ANSWERS

1. Mary Smith 2. Martine McCutcheon 3. Alex Ferns 4. Ferreira 5. Trinidad 6. Ashtray 7. Charlie Slater 8. Gary Hobbs 9. Pete Beale 10. Janine Evans

QUIZ 269

1. In which TV series did *Coronation Street* star Andrew Whyment play the best friend of Ralf Little?
2. Who wrote the TV series *Fat Friends*?
3. What nickname was given to CID officer Kerry Holmes in *The Bill*?
4. *Call Oxbridge 2000* was a belated spin-off of which soap?
5. Which Peter played Pete Beale in *EastEnders*?
6. Which Weatherfield resident owned a pair of garden gnomes called Guinevere and Arthur?
7. Which *Hollyoaks* character has a sister called Sophie, a brother called Justin and a mother called Liz?
8. In *Brookside*, which member of the Jordache family was played by Gillian Hanna?
9. In *EastEnders*, whom did Lorna Cartwright have an affair with after meeting him at an AA meeting?
10. In *Hollyoaks* was Gordon Cunningham's middle name Horace, Hubert or Hilton?

ANSWERS

1. *The Royle Family* 2. Kay Mellor 3. Sherlock 4. *Emergency Ward 10* 5. Peter Dean 6. Derek Wilton 7. Melanie Burton 8. Brenna Jordache 9. Phil Mitchell 10. Hilton

QUIZ 270

1 Which *Neighbours* character fell into a coma following a 1998 car accident?

2 Which US soap saw a cast member confined to the Brooktree Psychiatric Hospital?

3 Which star of *EastEnders* was voted Sexiest Male Actor at the 2002 British Soap Awards?

4 Who kidnapped Weatherfield baby Bethany Platt shortly after her birth?

5 Which star of *EastEnders* was voted Sexiest Female Actor at the 2002 British Soap Awards?

6 Which soap featured tear-jerking scenes involving the death of Batley the dog?

7 In which soap does Stuart Manning play the role of Sam Armstrong?

8 Which *Coronation Street* role is played by Scott Wright?

9 Which US first lady did the cast of *Grange Hill* meet during their anti-drugs campaign?

10 In which soap was Yasmin Mackenzie punched on her wedding day?

ANSWERS

1. Ben Atkins 2. *Dallas* 3. Martin Kemp 4. Alison Webster 5. Jessie Wallace 6. *Emmerdale* 7. *Night And Day* 8. Sam Kingston 9. Nancy Reagan 10. *Hollyoaks*

QUIZ 271

1 What is the name of Roy Cropper's café?

2 Was *Coronation Street* built in 1902, 1912 or 1922?

3 Who was Vicky McDonald's natural grandfather?

4 In 2004, which Lancashire-born comedian guested in *Coronation Street* as Eric Gartside?

5 Coronation Street was named in honour of the coronation of which king?

6 What is the name of the taxi firm owned and managed by Steve McDonald and Dev Alahan?

7 Which Weatherfield role is played by Shobna Gulati?

8 Which former *Street* star wrote a book expose entitled *The Secrets Of The Street*?

9 Which Welsh holiday town did Irma Barlow move to when she left Weatherfield?

10 Whom did Alf Roberts marry in 1978?

ANSWERS

1. Roy's Rolls 2. 1902 3. Alec Gilroy 4. Peter Kay 5. Edward VII 6. Streetcars 7. Sunita Parekh 8. Lynne Perrie 9. Llandudno 10. Renee Bradshaw

QUIZ 272

1. Which *Home And Away* character shared a prison cell with Vinnie Patterson?
2. In which soap did Derek Warner murder Harry Mowlem?
3. Which former *Neighbours* star, appeared as Caractacus Potts in a 2004 stage production of *Chitty Chitty Bang Bang*?
4. Which Rovers Return barmaid left Weatherfield after falling in love with Peter Shaw?
5. Which soap features a store called Drive N Buy?
6. In what year did the *Coronation Street* killer Richard Hillman first appear in Weatherfield?
7. Who was revealed as the father of Bianca Butcher in *EastEnders*?
8. What was the name of Betty Turpin's first husband in *Coronation Street*?
9. Who has played Belinda Slater in *EastEnders* and Charlotte Day in *Family Affairs*?
10. Which *Neighbours* character played by Alan Fletcher is an alcoholic?

ANSWERS

1. Jesse McGregor 2. *Emmerdale* 3. Jason Donovan 4. Gloria Todd 5. *Hollyoaks* 6. 2001 7. David Wicks 8. Cyril 9. Leanne Lakey 10. Karl Kennedy

QUIZ 273

1 In *EastEnders,* what connects David Samuels and Steve Khan?

2 In which soap was Shauna kidnapped by the Phillips brothers?

3 What is Charlie short for in the name of the *Dallas* character Charlie Wade?

4 Which coffee company signed a sponsorship deal to promote *Hollyoaks* in 2002?

5 In 2003 Steve McDonald employed Tracy Barlow as a what?

6 In which country was the funeral of the *EastEnders* character Frank Butcher held?

7 Whichsurname links the *Peyton Place* characters Sandy, Lee and Chris?

8 In *Emmerdale,* who cancelled his dream wedding to Tricia Stokes in 2002?

9 Which *EastEnders* character died of liver failure in 2002?

10 Who died first in *Coronation Street*: Alf Roberts, Samir Rachid or Maxine Peacock?

ANSWERS

1. Both doctors 2. *Home And Away* 3. Charlotte 4. Nescafe 5. Taxi driver 6. Spain 7. Webber 8. Marlon Dingle 9. Angie Watts 10. Samir Rachid

QUIZ 274

1 What is the name of the local newspaper in *EastEnders*?

2 What is the name of Nick Cotton's deceased son?

3 Whom was Kat Slater about to marry when the ceremony was stopped by Alfie Moon?

4 What is the name of the oldest member of the Tavernier children played by Steve Woodcock?

5 Who hired a hitman to kill Ian Beale?

6 What role is played by Christopher Parker in *EastEnders*?

7 What was Della Alexander's job in Albert Square?

8 What is the name of Steve Owen's sister?

9 Who served a three-year jail sentence for shooting Jack Dalton?

10 Which great-great-granddaughter of Queen Victoria visited the set of *EastEnders* in 2001?

ANSWERS

1. *Walford Gazette* 2. Ashley 3. Andy Hunter 4 Clyde 5. His wife Cindy 6. Spencer Moon 7. Hairdresser 8. Jackie 9. Dennis Rickman 10. Queen Elizabeth II

QUIZ 275

1 What is Libby Kennedy's job in *Neighbours*?

2 What was Fred short for in the name of the *Brookside* character Fred Gonzalez?

3 In which soap did Maureen Smart attempt to woo Alf Stewart?

4 On which romantic date did Dot Cotton marry Jim Branning in 2002?

5 Tony, Jill and Pat are members of which long-running soap farm family?

6 Which member of the Dingle clan died in August 1994?

7 Which *EastEnders* star played the role of Hassan B in the comedy movie *Ali G In Da House*?

8 What is the name of Helen and Gordon Cunningham's baby son in *Hollyoaks*?

9 In *EastEnders*, in which forest was Steve Owen's murdered girlfriend Saskia buried?

10 Who waved goodbye to Emily Bishop and Weatherfield to embark on a spiritual quest to India?

ANSWERS

1. Teacher 2. Frederico 3. *Home And Away* 4. Valentine's Day (Feb 14th) 5. *The Archers* 6. Ben Dingle 7. Ray Panthaki 8. Tom 9. Epping Forest 10. Spider Nugent

QUIZ 276

1. Delta Rho Farm was the name of a stables in which US soap?
2. At what number of Albert Square do Dot and Jim Branning share a home?
3. In which country is *The Far Pavillions* set?
4. What was the title of the 2002 *EastEnders* spin-off that co-starred Sid Owen and Patsy Palmer?
5. Who was the first actor to play Nick Tilsley in *Coronation Street*?
6. In which 1990s US soap did Lesley Anne Down play the role of Olivia Richards?
7. In *Neighbours*, who refused to marry Dr Tyler after learning of his infidelity?
8. In *EastEnders*, who had three children called Ian, Simon and David and two wives called Pat and Kathy?
9. In which soap did Hayley Smith fall in love with Alex?
10. Which *Brookside* character has had the surnames of Jordache, Wright and Dixon?

ANSWERS

1. *Dynasty* 2. Number 25 3. India 4. *Ricky And Bianca* 5. Warren Jackson 6. *Sunset Beach* 7. Tess Bell 8. Pete Beale 9. *Home And Away* 10. Rachel

QUIZ 277

1. Who was appointed Mayor of Weatherfield in 1973?
2. Who plays the corner shop owner Dev Alahan?
3. In *Coronation Street*, who battled for the affections of Fiz Brown with Tyrone Dobbs?
4. What was Claire Casey's occupation in Weatherfield?
5. On what day of the week was the very first episode of *Coronation Street* screened?
6. Which *Coronation Street* regular shared a flat over the corner shop with Shirley Armitage?
7. At which university did Andy McDonald begin a course in computer studies?
8. Which business partner of Len Fairclough died of a heart attack in 1977?
9. Which *Coronation Street* resident studied environmental issues at Manchester Polytechnic?
10. Is Raquel Wolstenhulme's middle name Kerry, Katherine or Kimberley?

ANSWERS

1. Alf Roberts 2. Jimmi Harkishin 3. Kirk Sutherland 4. Nanny 5. Friday 6. Curly Watts 7. Sheffield University 8. Jerry Booth 9. Jenny Bradley 10. Katherine

QUIZ 278

1. Which soap features a business called Tate Haulage?
2. Which Australian soap spanned 692 episodes from 1979 to 1986?
3. Which song became a hit record for Buddy Holly in 1959 and the title of a soap in 1992?
4. Which Frankie Laine hit was covered by *Soldier Soldier* stars Robson and Jerome in 1995?
5. What was Polly Becker's job in *EastEnders*?
6. What colour provides the first name of the actor who played Al Baker in *Knot's Landing*?
7. Who fell into a coma in *EastEnders* after being beaten up by Grant Mitchell, following an affair with Sharon?
8. Which California-based soap featured the characters of Dr Foster and Sheriff Jack North?
9. In *EastEnders,* what is the name of Dennis Rickman's mother?
10. Which wife of *London's Burning* creator Jack Rosenthal starred as a publican in *Coronation Street*?

ANSWERS

1. *Emmerdale* 2. *Prisoner Cell Block H* 3. *Heartbeat* 4. 'I Believe' 5. Journalist 6. Red (Red Buttons) 7. Phil Mitchell 8. *Falcon Crest* 9. Paula 10. Maureen Lipman

QUIZ 279

1 In which British city was the rag trade soap *Connie* set?

2 Who died first in *EastEnders*: Ethel Skinner, Frank Butcher or Tiffany Mitchell?

3 Who played Bert Tilsley in *Coronation Street*?

4 Who played Bert Tilsley's son Brian?

5 In *EastEnders*, which member of the di Marco family was arrested in Norfolk on drugs charges?

6 In *Hollyoaks* who has romanced Jill, Celia, Jacqui and Patti?

7 Which series has featured the characters of Father Kelly, Dr Reeve and Reverend Winters?

8 Was *Peyton Place* set in New York, New Jersey or New England?

9 In *Emmerdale*, which member of the Sugden family is played by Kelvin Fletcher?

10 Which US soap character wears a watch bearing the inscription "If you will, it is no dream"?

ANSWERS

1.Nottingham 2.Tiffany Mitchell 3.Peter Dudley 4.Christopher Quentin 5.Teresa 6.Jack Osborne 7.*Peak Practice* 8.New England 9.Andy Sugden 10.Dawson Leery in *Dawson's Creek*

QUIZ 280

1 Who drove the car that killed Tiffany Mitchell?

2 Who plays the Walford role of Little Mo?

3 What is the name of Ricky Butcher's son?

4 Who left Albert Square on a motorbike in 2003?

5 Who proposed to Sonia Jackson in 2002?

6 Which café owner was played by Nejdet Salih?

7 What is the name of Robbie Jackson's mother?

8 In *EastEnders*, who married Mel, Cindy and Laura?

9 What was the job of Matthew Rose at the nightclub owned by Steve Owen?

10 What was the name of Beppe di Marco's mother?

ANSWERS

1. Frank Butcher 2. Kacey Ainsworth 3. Liam 4. Mark Fowler 5. Jamie Mitchell 6. Ali Osman 7. Carol 8. Ian Beale 9. Disc jockey 10. Rosa

QUIZ 281

1. In *Emmerdale*, who killed Ray Mullen?
2. Justin Burton and Ali Taylor both attend which soap school?
3. Which *Coronation Street* character served as an NCO in the Royal Army Catering Corps?
4. In *Brookside*, was Geoff Rogers nicknamed Growler, Grinder or Gaffer?
5. Which soap featured a Manchester café owner called Peggy Sagar?
6. Who composed the *EastEnders* theme music?
7. What type of shop is found at the address 13 Turpin Rd, Walford?
8. Which soap features a hospital porter called Ken Hopkirk?
9. What did Tracy Barlow sell to the Croppers for £15,000?
10. In which soap does Isabel Morgan run the village store?

ANSWERS

1.Louise Appleton 2.Hollyoaks Comprehensive 3. Percy Sugden 4. Growler 5. *Albion Market* 6. Simon May 7. Bookmakers 8. *The Royal* 9. Her baby 10. *High Road*

QUIZ 282

1. Which star of *Hollyoaks* was born Bernard Jewry?
2. Which series first screened in 2004, tells the story of life on board HMS *Suffolk*?
3. Who bought the Rovers Return in December 1998?
4. In *Dallas,* was Miss Ellie Ewing's presumed dead brother called Garfield, Garrison or Gilbert?
5. Which former star of *Eldorado* played the new manager of Earl's Park FC in the third series of *Footballers' Wives*?
6. Which US series featured a beauty spot called Lake Kezia?
7. In which town is the Scottish soap *River City* set?
8. What job was held by Annabelle Collins in *Brookside*?
9. Which *Coronation Street* bigamist was played by George Waring?
10. Which school pupil landed Ken Barlow in trouble in 2002 after he struck him?

ANSWERS

1. Alvin Stardust 2. *Making Waves* 3. Natalie Horrocks 4. Garrison 5. Jesse Birdsall 6. *The Little House On The Prairie* 7. Shieldinch 8. Magistrate 9. Arnold Swain 10. Aidan Critchley

QUIZ 283

In *Coronation Street* …

1. Who eloped with Steve McDonald on her 18th birthday?
2. Why did the Websters call their first daughter Rosie?
3. Who took a brief trip to a prison cell in 2004 after clipping Chesney Brown around the ear?
4. In 2004, who planted a bottle of vodka on Janice Battersby, in an attempt to get her the sack?
5. Who proposed to Sally Webster in 2001?
6. Who left *Coronation Street* in 1997, to move into sheltered accommodation at Mayfield Court?
7. In which year did Alma Baldwin die?
8. Which Weatherfield resident has an adopted son called Stephen Reid?
9. Whom did Natalie Horrocks marry in 1998?
10. Who was murdered by Darren Whitely?

ANSWERS

1. Vicky Arden 2. She was delivered in a taxi on Rosamund Street 3. Rita Sullivan 4. Nick Tilsley 5. Danny Hargreaves 6. Percy Sugden 7. 2001 8. Audrey Roberts 9. Des Barnes 10. Brian Tilsley

QUIZ 284

1. Which star of *The Bill* joined the cast of *EastEnders* as John Davis?
2. In which soap does Cheryl Barker work as a DC for the Metropolitan police?
3. What was Alison Webster's maiden name before her short-lived Weatherfield marriage to Kevin Webster?
4. In *EastEnders*, who is the older brother – Gianni or Beppe?
5. Which role was played by Charles Dale in *Coronation Street*?
6. Which *Emmerdale* MP faked her own death in 2003?
7. In which country does Kenny, the older brother of Pete Beale, live?
8. Which *Neighbours* character played by Tony Bonner is nicknamed Cookie?
9. Which US soap featured a thoroughfare called Seaview Circle?
10. As a teenager, who sang in a female pop trio called Milan, before finding fame in Walford?

ANSWERS

1. Huw Higginson 2. *Family Affairs* 3. Wakefield 4. Beppe 5. Dennis Stringer 6. Gloria Pollard 7. New Zealand 8. Martin Cook 9. *Knot's Landing* 10. Martine McCutcheon

QUIZ 285

1. Which soap pub was devastated by a lightning storm on New Year's Eve 2003?
2. In *Coronation Street*, which actor played Ted Sullivan, the second husband of Rita?
3. In *EastEnders,* what is the name of Steve Owen's mother?
4. Which Rovers Return employee married Billy Williams in 1997?
5. Who played the role of Cinders in the TV series *Roughnecks*?
6. In *EastEnders,* what is the name of Tiffany Mitchell's father?
7. In which soap were the characters of Jack Vincent and Anna Paul killed off in 2003?
8. In *Coronation Street*, which wife of Fred Gee was killed in a factory fire in 1975?
9. Which county connects *Emmerdale, All Creatures Great And Small* and *Heartbeat*?
10. Which musical instrument does Sonia Jackson play in *EastEnders*?

ANSWERS

1. The Woolpack 2. William Russell 3. Barbara 4. Betty Turpin 5. Ricky Tomlinson 6. Raymond 7. *Casualty* 8. Edna 9. Yorkshire 10. Trumpet

QUIZ 286

1. Who plays the gangster Andy Hunter in *EastEnders*?
2. Who set fire to the nightclub Angie's Den?
3. On which day of the year did Alfie Moon marry Kat Slater?
4. Who was Barry Evans' first wife?
5. Which character, played by Sean Maguire, had his dream of playing for Walford Town FC curtailed by injury?
6. Which Walford resident married an illegal immigrant in 1993?
7. What surname is shared by the Walford characters Simon, Susan and Matthew?
8. What did Michelle Fowler's surname become upon her first marriage?
9. Which member of the Jackson family was played by Howard Anthony?
10. Whom did Peggy Mitchell marry in 1999?

ANSWERS

1. Michael Higgs 2. Billy Mitchell 3. Christmas Day 4. Natalie Price 5. Aidan Brosnan 6. Phil Mitchell 7. Rose 8. Holloway 9. Alan Jackson 10. Frank Butcher

QUIZ 287

1 Which song, originally a hit for Brian Hyland, was covered by the soap actor Jason Donovan?

2 Which actor, who played Alan Sinclair in *Peak Practice*, won a 2004 BAFTA for his role in the film *Love Actually*?

3 Where did Alfie Moon marry Kat Slater?

4 Which building in *Emmerdale* bears the date AD1826 above its front entrance?

5 Which Oscar-winning actor married *Home And Away* star Danielle Spencer in 2003?

6 In which soap did Terry Sullivan propose to Michelle Jones?

7 Which militant employee of Mike Baldwin is played by Helene Palmer?

8 Which star of *Dallas* was born Priscilla Beaulieu?

9 In *EastEnders,* who drove the car that killed Jamie Mitchell?

10 Which soap pub is haunted by a one-armed drummer?

ANSWERS

1. *Sealed With A Kiss* 2. Bill Nighy 3. The Queen Vic 4. Beckindale School 5. Russell Crowe 6. *Brookside* 7. Ida Clough 8. Priscilla Presley 9. Martin Fowler 10. The Bull in *The Archers*

QUIZ 288

1. On which Caribbean island did Vicky marry Steve McDonald in *Coronation Street*?
2. In which year of the 1990s did Haley Patterson move to *Coronation Street*?
3. In *The Bill*, what is the name of the neighbouring police station to Sun Hill?
4. What is the first name of the *Neighbours* character nicknamed Stingray?
5. Joyce Smedley is the mother of which Weatherfield resident?
6. Which *EastEnders* character died during childbirth on Bonfire Night 1998?
7. In *Coronation Street*, which member of the Barlow clan was played by Noel Dyson?
8. Who played Wallis Simpson in the TV series *Edward And Mrs Simpson*?
9. Which Walford resident died of a heart attack in May 2003?
10. Which soap character has run bars in Spain, Brighton, the Canaries and Weatherfield?

ANSWERS

1. St Lucia 2. 1998 3. Barton Street 4. Scott 5. Judy Mallett 6. Cindy Beale 7. Ida Barlow 8. Cynthia Harris 9. Roy Evans 10. Bet Lynch

QUIZ 289

1 Who composed the *Coronation Street* theme?

2 Lorraine Brownlow was the niece of which Weatherfield resident?

3 Whom did Alf Roberts sell his corner shop to, when he sold it for the first time?

4 Whom did Alf Roberts sell his corner shop to, when he sold it for the second time?

5 Which member of the Harris family is played by Richard Fleeshman?

6 Which *Street* star also plays the role of Bill McQueen in *Doctors*?

7 What did Don Brennan have amputated in 1992?

8 Who married Angela Hawthorne in 1995 and divorced her in 1999?

9 In which British city did Roy and Hayley Cropper enjoy their honeymoon?

10 Which knighted newsreader appeared as himself in *Coronation Street*?

ANSWERS

1. Eric Spear 2. Natalie Barnes 3. Brendan Scott 4. Reg Holdsworth 5. Craig Harris 6. Charles Lawson 7. His left foot 8. Norris Cole 9. York 10. Sir Trevor McDonald

QUIZ 290

1. Which soap features a radio station called UNI FM?
2. Which Weatherfield gangster was played by Glyn Grain?
3. From which slimming disease did *EastEnders* character Kim McFarlane suffer?
4. In *Hollyoaks,* what is the name of Gordon Cunningham's son played by Matt Littler?
5. In 1998 who was elected as councillor for Weatherfield St Mary's Ward?
6. In which city is Grange Hill School?
7. Which soap ended its 21-year run with Jimmy, Sean, Martin, Tim and Steve lynching a drug dealer?
8. Whom did Tracy Barlow marry in a fixed marriage in 2003?
9. Which war causes *EastEnders* character Grant Mitchell recurring nightmares?
10. In *Coronation Street,* which of the McDonald twins was born first, Andy or Steve?

ANSWERS

1. *Neighbours* 2. Fraser Henderson 3. Bulimia 4. Max 5. Audrey Roberts 6. London 7. *Brookside* 8. Roy Cropper 9. Falklands War 10. Andy

QUIZ 291

1 In *Holby City* what is the job of Lisa Fox?

2 Which soap features a landmark called the Hassett Hills?

3 In *EastEnders*, which member of the Jackson family was briefly engaged to Kerry Skinner?

4 In *Coronation Street*, was Sally Whittaker's mother called Edna, Elsie or Elizabeth?

5 Which breed of dog was Batley in *Emmerdale*?

6 Jane Tennison is the lead character of which long-running series?

7 In *Coronation Street*, which married couple made the mistake of eating cannabis cake in 2003?

8 In which soap is Lesley Ash married to Phil Middlemiss?

9 In *EastEnders*, what was the name of Gita Kapoor's unfaithful husband?

10 Which member of Erinsborough's Hoyland family is played by Kyal Marsh?

ANSWERS

1. Midwife 2. *The Archers* 3. Robbie Jackson 4. Elsie 5. Yorkshire terrier 6. *Prime Suspect* 7. Jack and Vera Duckworth 8. *Where The Heart Is* 9. Sanjay 10. Boyd Hoyland

QUIZ 292

1. Which member of the Fowler family is played by Scarlett Johnson?
2. Which European capital city did Diane Butcher leave Albert Square for?
3. At which school was Etta Tavernier made acting head?
4. After whom did Ethel Skinner name her pet pug?
5. In the 1990s who had an on/off relationship with Debbie Tyler?
6. What was the nationality of the Walford character Huw Edwards?
7. Which actor turned up in Walford in 2003 playing a ruthless gangster called Jack Dalton?
8. What was the name of Sue and Ali Osman's baby that tragically died?
9. Whom did Lynne Slater marry in 2001?
10. In which year did *EastEnders* celebrate its 10th anniversary?

ANSWERS

1. Vicki Fowler 2. Paris 3. Walford Primary School 4. Her deceased husband Willy 5. Nigel Bates 6. Welsh 7. Hywel Bennett 8. Hassan 9. Gary Hobbs 10. 1995

QUIZ 293

1. Who plays Lucy Barlow in *Coronation Street*?
2. What was the first name of the *Brookside* character whose surnames have been Corkhill, Stanlow and Phelan?
3. Who is the only *Coronation Street* character to have been awarded an OBE?
4. Did *Ally McBeal* make its TV debut in 1996, 1997 or 1998?
5. Who died first in *EastEnders*: Arthur Fowler, Pete Beale or Eddie Royle?
6. Who played Carly Reynolds in *Beverly Hills 90210* and went on to become an Oscar-winning film star?
7. Where did *EastEnders* character Nigel Bates move to after falling in love with a teacher called Julie Hay?
8. Jack Osborne is the landlord of which soap pub?
9. In which city was the short-lived soap *Empire Road* set?
10. Which star of *The Last Of The Summer Wine* played Charlie Dickinson in *Coronation Street*?

ANSWERS

1. Katy Carmichael 2. Lindsey 3. Alf Roberts 4. 1997 5. Eddie Royle 6. Hilary Swank 7. Scotland 8. The Dog In The Pond in *Hollyoaks* 9. Birmingham 10. Bill Owen

QUIZ 294

1 In *EastEnders*, what is the name of Tom Banks' stepdaughter?

2 Which *Coronation Street* character was murdered by Joe Donelli?

3 What is the surname of the *Emmerdale* family that arrived in the soap after winning the *Soapstars* TV reality show?

4 In which country was the TV mini-series *Shogun* set?

5 In *EastEnders*, what was the real first name of the character of Precious Hudson?

6 Which *Emmerdale* regular married Rachel Hughes in 1995?

7 In *Neighbours*, how is Serena Bishop related to Sky Mangel?

8 What is the surname of the *Family Affairs* sisters Chloe and Melanie?

9 What is the first name of the *Neighbours* character nicknamed Stonefish?

10 What is the first name of the *Neighbours* character nicknamed Toadfish?

ANSWERS

1. Charlotte 2. Steve Tanner 3. Jardines 4. Japan 5. Marjorie 6. Chris Tate 7. Cousins 8. Costello 9. Kevin 10. Jarrod

QUIZ 295

1 Who was *Coronation Street*'s first transexual character?

2 What was the name of Maureen Holdsworth's disabled mother?

3 Which *Street* character served as an engineer in the Royal Signals?

4 What was the name of Richard Hillman's ex-wife, whom he killed with a fatal blow from a spade?

5 Who plays the role of Cilla Brown in *Coronation Street*?

6 What was Maureen's surname before her marriage to Reg Holdsworth?

7 Who married Evelyn Sykes in 2001?

8 Who played the Rovers barmaid Tina Fowler?

9 Which south-coast city did Alec Gilroy move to in 1992?

10 Which wife of Mike Baldwin was played by Shirin Taylor?

ANSWERS

1. Hayley Patterson 2. Maud Grimes 3. Jim McDonald 4. Patricia 5. Wendi Peters 6. Naylor 7. Fred Elliott 8. Michelle Holmes 9. Southampton 10. Jackie Ingram

QUIZ 296

1 Which medical series features a hospital called St Victors?

2 What is the name of Jade Sullivan's stroppy sister in *Home And Away*?

3 In *Coronation Street*, Deirdre's third husband Samir was born in which country?

4 Which was the first US soap to be screened in colour?

5 Which award-winning series ended with the funeral of Rachel Bradley?

6 Which DC left Sun Hill's CID to join Scotland Yard's Fine Art Squad?

7 Who was the chief bridesmaid when Bet Lynch married Alec Gilroy?

8 Which soap features a Greek restaurant called Heliopolis?

9 What was the title of the 1972 revival of *Dr Kildare*?

10 When the TV series *All Creatures Great And Small* began, in which decade was it set?

ANSWERS

1. *A & E* 2. Kirsty 3. Morocco 4. *As The World Turns* 5. *Cold Feet* 6. Mike Dashwood 7. Gloria Todd 8. *Emmerdale* 9. *Young Dr Kildare* 10. 1930s

QUIZ 297

1. Who played the role of Spock in *All Quiet On The Preston Front*?
2. In 1979, who was voted Man Of The Year by the Dallas Civic Group?
3. Which *Coronation Street* favourite had the catchphrase "Well, I don't really know"?
4. What type of shop stands at 11 Turpin St, Walford?
5. Which character, played by Margot Bryant, left Weatherfield in 1976?
6. Who has played the roles of Carol in *Fat Friends*, Lorna in *EastEnders* and Elaine in *The Two Of Us*?
7. Who attended Albert Square's 2004 Valentine Ball with Sonia Jackson?
8. What first name is shared by a Simpson in *Brookside*, a Sullivan in *EastEnders* and a Hunter in *Hollyoaks*?
9. Which *Coronation Street* star was born Cathryn Helen Wigglesworth?
10. On whose novels were the series *Poirot* and *Miss Marple* based?

ANSWERS

1. Stephen Tompkinson 2. Cliff Barnes 3. Mavis Wilton 4. Video rental 5. Minnie Caldwell 6. Janet Dibley 7. Martin Fowler 8. Dan 9. Helen Worth 10. Agatha Christie

QUIZ 298

1. Did Benny Hawkins first appear in *Crossroads* in 1973, 1974 or 1975?
2. In *Dallas*, is Cliff Barnes' favourite food Chinese, Italian or Indian?
3. In *Coronation Street*, is the football team called Weatherfield United, Weatherfield County or Weatherfield City?
4. How many episodes of *Eldorado* were made: 56, 156 or 256?
5. How many *Carry On* films did *EastEnders* star Barbara Windsor appear in: nine, ten or eleven?
6. Is Gary Ewing's middle name Alfred, Albert or Arthur?
7. Was *EastEnders* star Dean Gaffney born in the 1960s, 1970s or 1980s?
8. Was the Walton's family cow called Lucky, Chance or Fortune?
9. For how many episodes was *Coronation Street* originally intended to run: eleven, twelve or thirteen?
10. In which city did Hayley Patterson undergo a gender reassignment operation: Amsterdam, Paris or Brussels?

ANSWERS

1. 1975 2. Chinese 3. Weatherfield County 4. 156 5. Nine 6. Arthur 7. 1970s 8. Chance 9. Thirteen 10 Amsterdam

QUIZ 299

1 Who plays Jim Branning in *EastEnders*?

2 Which Chief Superintendant was played by Peter Ellis in *The Bill*?

3 Who played Roy in *The Bill*, Gordon in *Heartbeat* and Josh in *Casualty*?

4 Which soap features two prison inmates called 'the two Julies'?

5 What was the former name of Angie's Den in *EastEnders*?

6 In which soap did Adam Chance manage a health club?

7 In which city is the TV series *Cutting* It set?

8 Who was left 10 percent of the voting shares in the will of Jock Ewing?

9 Which soap features a school called Hotten Comprehensive?

10 Who plays Jane Tennison in *Prime Suspect*?

ANSWERS

1. John Bardon 2. CS Brownlow 3. Ian Bleasdale 4. *Bad Girls* 5. E20 6. *Crossroads* 7. Manchester 8. Ray Krebbs 9. *Emmerdale* 10. Helen Mirren

QUIZ 300

1 In US soaps, who has played the mother of John Ross Ewing and the mother or Amanda Woodward?

2 Which song from an Andrew Lloyd Webber musical was a No 1 hit for Jason Donovan?

3 In *Footballers' Wives*, what is the name of Earl Park FC's Italian midfield star?

4 What is the home city of *EastEnders* character Kate Mitchell?

5 Who has played the roles of Alex in *Eldorado* and Charlie in *EastEnders*?

6 In *Coronation Street*, who was Leanne Battersby's drug dealer?

7 What was Lisa's maiden name before her marriage to Mark Fowler in *EastEnders*?

8 Which Asian country did the *Emmerdale* character Tricia Dingle move to for six months in 2003?

9 In *Dynasty*, what is the name of Blake Carrington's oldest son?

10 Which character, played by Lynne McGranger in *Home And Away*, fought back from alcoholism?

ANSWERS

1. Linda Gray 2. 'Any Dream Will Do' 3. Salvatore Biagi 4. Newcastle 5. Derek Martin 6. Jez Quigley 7. Shaw 8. India 9. Adam 10. Irene Roberts